Astronomy

E. G. Ebbighausen

University of Oregon

CHARLES E. MERRILL BOOKS, INC., COLUMBUS, OHIO

Merrill Physical Science Series

Robert J. Foster and Walter A. Gong, *Editors*

San Jose State College

Library of Congress Catalog Card Number: 66-14394

PRINTED IN THE UNITED STATES OF AMERICA

Editors' Foreword

As curricula become more crowded in this age of rapidly expanding knowledge and specialization, more and more colleges and universities are turning to integrated interdisciplinary courses to transmit the basic essentials of science to non-science majors. We believe that the rigid structure of most physical science textbooks has imposed severe limitations on instruction in these courses. Far too often, instructors trained in various specialities have had to attempt to fit the wide range of goals, abilities, and backgrounds of their students to a textbook, when the converse, of course, would be much more satisfactory.

In January, 1965, the editors, five authors, and representatives of Charles E. Merrill Books, Inc., met in San Francisco to implement a new conception of physical science textbooks. The result is the *Physical Science Series,* a collection of specially written, integrated materials in short, paperback form for the college physical science program. Our coordinated efforts were directed by three vital principles.

1. The Series permits maximum flexibility of use by instructors and students. Each paperback textbook represents a five-to-seven-week section of instruction, and may be used in any sequence or combination desired by the instructor. In addition, freedom of sequence within a single book is possible. This flexibility is especially helpful in courses that include laboratory experience. In this way it is hoped that each instructor will be free to choose the most appropriate materials for his students.

2. The subject areas are portrayed in a valid manner. Each book is written by a specialist in a different discipline—physicist, chemist, astronomer, meteorologist, geologist, and science educator. Thus, in place of a homogeneous blend of textbook statements, the individual paperback textbooks have distinctive scientific flavors. The student can discover both the contrasts and underlying unities in the viewpoints of scientists in different disciplines; he can, for example, compare the approach of the physicist, who performs lab-

oratory experiments, with that of the geologist, who depends largely on observations of natural occurrences.

3. Scientific communication is clear, concise, and correct. Each author is both academician and experienced teacher. He has designed instruction around carefully selected scientific principles logically related to laws, definitions, and associated phenomena. Technology is used to provide illustrative examples rather than a myriad of facts to be remembered. Mathematical reasoning is used only when the sciences are made more (not less) understandable for the non-science major. Scientific jargon and excessive nomenclature are avoided.

San Jose, California   *Robert J. Foster*

Walter A. Gong

Table of Contents

Chapter 1
THE BEGINNINGS OF ASTRONOMY—*Ptolemy to Newton*   **1**

1-1   THE EARLIEST ASTRONOMICAL OBSERVATIONS   2
1-2   THE GEOCENTRIC SYSTEM. PTOLEMY   2
1-3   THE INNER PLANETS: MERCURY AND VENUS   3
1-4   THE MOTION OF THE MOON AND THE SUN   4
1-5   THE OUTER PLANETS: MARS, JUPITER AND SATURN   4
1-6   RISING AND SETTING   5
1-7   COMMENTS ON THE PTOLEMAIC SYSTEM   5
1-8   THE HELIOCENTRIC, OR COPERNICAN, SYSTEM   6
1-9   RETROGRADE MOTION, COPERNICAN STYLE   6
1-10 TYCHO BRAHE (1546-1601)   7
1-11 JOHANNES KEPLER (1571-1630)   9
1-12 KEPLER'S FIRST LAW: THE FORM OF THE ORBIT   9
1-13 KEPLER'S SECOND LAW: THE LAW OF AREAS   10
1-14 KEPLER'S THIRD LAW: THE HARMONIC LAW   10
1-15 COMMENTS ON KEPLER'S LAWS   11
1-16 GALILEO GALILEI (1564-1642)   11
1-17 ISAAC NEWTON (1643-1727)   12
      QUESTIONS   13

Chapter 2
THE EARTH AND THE MOON   **14**

2-1   THE PROOFS OF THE ROTATION AND REVOLUTION
      OF THE EARTH   14
2-2   THE ORBIT OF THE EARTH   16
2-3   THE CELESTIAL SPHERE AND CELESTIAL COORDINATES   16
2-4   THE SEASONS   17

2-5   THE PRECESSION OF THE EQUINOXES   18
2-6   TIME   19
2-7   THE MOON   19
2-8   THE TIDES   20
2-9   THE PHASES OF THE MOON   21
2-10   THE TEMPERATURE OF THE MOON'S SURFACE   22
2-11   THE FACE OF THE MOON   22
2-12   THE ORIGIN OF THE MOON'S SURFACE FEATURES   23
2-13   ECLIPSES OF THE SUN AND THE MOON   26
2-14   THE IMPORTANCE OF ECLIPSES   27
       QUESTIONS   27

Chapter 3
THE TOOLS AND METHODS OF THE ASTRONOMER   28

3-1   LIGHT   28
3-2   REFLECTION, REFRACTION, AND DISPERSION   29
3-3   THE PRISM AND THE SPECTRUM   29
3-4   LENSES   30
3-5   LENS ABERRATIONS   30
3-6   IMAGE FORMATION BY LENSES   31
3-7   THE REFLECTING TELESCOPE   32
3-8   THE TYPES OF REFLECTING TELESCOPES   33
3-9   REFRACTING AND REFLECTING TELESCOPES
           CONTRASTED   33
3-10   RESOLUTION   36
3-11   THE SPECTROSCOPE   37
3-12   THE CONTINUOUS SPECTRUM   37
3-13   THE BRIGHT LINE SYSTEM   39
3-14   THE ABSORPTION SPECTRUM   40
3-15   THE ELEMENTS OF THE ATOMIC THEORY   42
3-16   A MORE EXTENDED VIEW OF THE NATURE OF LIGHT   43
3-17   ENERGY LEVELS IN ATOMS. THE ABSORPTION AND
           EMISSION OF LIGHT BY ATOMS   43
3-18   THE DOPPLER EFFECT. RADIAL VELOCITY   46
3-19   RADIO TELESCOPES   47
       QUESTIONS   49

Chapter 4
PLANETS AND SATELLITES; COMETS AND METEORS   50

4-1   THE SCALE OF THE SOLAR SYSTEM   50
4-2   MEASURING DISTANCES IN THE SOLAR SYSTEM   50

Contents   vii

4-3   TWO SOLAR FAMILIES   51
4-4   THE ASPECTS OF THE PLANETS. MERCURY AND VENUS.
       THE INFERIOR PLANETS   52
4-5   THE PHYSICAL NATURE OF MERCURY AND VENUS   53
4-6   MARS   54
4-7   THE TELESCOPIC APPEARANCE OF MARS   54
4-8   THE ATMOSPHERE AND TEMPERATURE OF MARS   54
4-9   LIFE ON MARS   56
4-10   THE RECENT MARINER IV OBSERVATIONS OF MARS   56
4-11   BODE'S LAW. THE ASTEROIDS   57
4-12   THE ASTEROIDS   57
4-13   THE ESCAPE OF ATMOSPHERES   58
4-14   JUPITER   59
4-15   SATURN   60
4-16   THE SATELLITE SYSTEMS OF JUPITER AND SATURN   62
4-17   URANUS AND NEPTUNE   62
4-18   THE DISCOVERIES OF URANUS, NEPTUNE AND PLUTO   62
4-19   THE DETERMINATION OF THE MASS OF A PLANET
       AND A SATELLITE   63
4-20   COMETS   64
4-21   THE ORBITS OF COMETS   64
4-22   THE CHANGES IN THE APPEARANCE OF A COMET   65
4-23   THE PHYSICAL NATURE OF A COMET   65
4-24   METEORS, METEOROIDS AND METEORITES   66
4-25   THE METEOROID IMPACT WITH THE EARTH'S ATMOS-
       PHERE   66
4-26   METEOR SWARMS   66
4-27   THE STRUCTURE AND COMPOSITION OF SWARM METE-
       OROIDS   67
4-28   THE RELATION BETWEEN SWARM METEOROIDS AND
       COMETS   67
4-29   METEORITES   68
4-30   METEORITE CRATERS   69
4-31   THE ORIGIN OF METEORITES   70
4-32   MICROMETEORITES   70
4-33   THE METEOROID HAZARD TO SPACE TRAVEL   70
4-34   THE 1908 SIBERIAN METEORITE (?)   71
4-35   THE ORIGIN AND EVOLUTION OF THE SOLAR SYSTEM   71
       The random capture hypothesis   71
       The encounter hypothesis   72
       The nebular hypothesis   72
       The proto-planet hypothesis   73
       QUESTIONS   75

Chapter 5
THE SUN. AN INTRODUCTION TO THE STARS   76

5-1	THE PHYSICAL STRUCTURE OF THE SUN	76
5-2	THE SURFACE PHENOMENA OF THE SUN	77
5-3	PROMINENCES	78
5-4	SOME SOLAR INSTRUMENTS	79
5-5	SOLAR FLARES	80
5-6	THE SOLAR CORONA	80
5-7	THE SUN SPOT CYCLE	81
5-8	THE SOLAR SPECTRUM	82
5-9	RADIO NOISE FROM THE SUN	82
5-10	THE EFFECTS OF SOLAR ACTIVITY ON THE EARTH	83
5-11	CONSTELLATIONS	83
5-12	STELLAR DISTANCES. THE STELLAR PARALLAX	84
5-13	RADIAL VELOCITY AND PROPER MOTION	84
5-14	THE STELLAR MAGNITUDE SYSTEM	85
5-15	APPARENT AND ABSOLUTE MAGNITUDES. THE DISTANCE MODULUS	85
5-16	STELLAR SPECTRA AND THE SPECTRAL SEQUENCE	86
5-17	THE INTERPRETATION OF THE SPECTRAL SEQUENCE	87
5-18	THE HERTZSPRUNG-RUSSELL DIAGRAM	88
5-19	SPECTROSCOPIC ABSOLUTE MAGNITUDES AND DISTANCES	90
5-20	THE MASS-LUMINOSITY RELATION AND THE LUMINOSITY FUNCTION	90
	QUESTIONS	90

Chapter 6
VARIETY AMONG STARS—*Stellar Systems*   92

6-1	VISUAL DOUBLE STARS	92
6-2	SPECTROSCOPIC BINARIES	93
6-3	ECLIPSING BINARIES	95
6-4	MILKY WAY CLUSTERS	96
6-5	GLOBULAR CLUSTERS	97
6-6	CEPHEID VARIABLES	98
	Classical Cepheids	99
	Short period Cepheids	99
6-7	THE PERIOD-LUMINOSITY RELATION	99
6-8	THE NOVAE: ORDINARY AND SUPER	100
6-9	THE CRAB NEBULA	101

6-10   OUR GALAXY: THE MILKY WAY   102
6-11   THE INTERSTELLAR MEDIUM   103
6-12   THE EVIDENCE FOR THE INTERSTELLAR MEDIUM   104
       Interstellar reddening   104
       Bright nebulae   104
       Interstellar absorption lines   105
       The radio emission of interstellar hydrogen   105
6-13   THE FORMATION OF STARS   105
6-14   NUCLEAR REACTIONS IN STARS AND STELLAR EVOLUTION   106
6-15   THE GALACTIC HALO   107
6-16   STELLAR POPULATION TYPES   107
       QUESTIONS   108

Chapter 7
GALAXIES AND COSMOLOGY   109

7-1   THE DISTANCE OF THE ANDROMEDA GALAXY   109
7-2   THE CLASSIFICATION OF GALAXIES   110
7-3   THE DETERMINATION OF THE DISTANCE TO GALAXIES   114
7-4   THE ABSOLUTE MAGNITUDES, DIMENSIONS AND MASSES
       OF GALAXIES   114
7-5   CLUSTERS OF GALAXIES. THE LOCAL GROUP   115
7-6   INTERGALACTIC MATTER   116
7-7   THE VELOCITY-DISTANCE RELATION. THE RED SHIFT   117
7-8   THE INTERPRETATION OF THE VELOCITY-DISTANCE
       RELATION   117
7-9   COSMOLOGY   118
7-10   THE OSCILLATING UNIVERSE   119
7-11   THE STEADY STATE THEORY   120
7-12   EXTRAGALACTIC RADIO SOURCES   120
7-13   THE ORIGIN AND EVOLUTION OF GALAXIES   122
       QUESTIONS   123

Appendix 1
SUGGESTED READINGS   124

Appendix 2
STAR MAPS   125

INDEX   131

Chapter 1

The Beginnings of Astronomy—
Ptolemy to Newton

The fascination that most people feel for astronomy arises from the very special nature of astronomy's concern for the remote and inaccessible regions of the universe. The chemist, physicist, biologist or archeologist can actually handle and study—in the field or the laboratory—those samples of nature that are of interest to him. But an astronomer can do this only when he has in hand a fragment of meteoric material. For the rest, he must study the light of the celestial objects and, with the aid of rather special techniques, attempt to derive useful information and ideas. The average person suspects a touch of magic in the astronomer's work; he may even think that astronomers must be smarter than other scientists—this is probably not true, but one can make a good case for their being the most ingenious. If so, it is because they must be. Their accomplishments are the result of frequent borrowing from the mathematicians, physicists, chemists, geologists and engineers. But the astronomers have given in return.

The most absorbing discoveries in astronomy are relatively recent. Man's knowledge of astronomy in Christ's day was not much less than in A.D. 1600, but in the latter year it was so vastly less than it is now that we should examine the reasons. In part, the enormous progress of the last three and one-half centuries is due to instruments such as the telescope first used by Galileo in 1610. His small spyglass may be contrasted with the immense 200-inch Hale reflector on Mt. Palomar whose moving parts weigh 600 tons. To a large extent this advance was an engineering achievement. Developments in mathematics were another great boost. These began with the discovery of the calculus in the 17th century by Newton and Leibnitz and its application to all branches of the physical sciences. But the greatest change of all was in attitude and point of view, in the idea that man must be at the center of his universal environment and that his position in the universe is a very special one. Real advancement began about A.D. 1600 when man became willing to consider the revolutionary concept that he was not in the center of the universe.

1

In the main, this chapter covers that period beginning about A.D. 150, when Ptolemy wrote his famous book on the geocentric system, and concluding in the 17th century with Isaac Newton's mathematical formulation of the law of universal gravitation.

1-1   The Earliest Astronomical Observations

From the very earliest times man observed the celestial bodies. Certainly among the first of these were the rising and setting of the sun, moon and stars, and the phases of the moon. To these would be added in time the seasonal changes in the sun's noon altitude and the points on the horizon where the sun rises. The idea of *fixed stars,* and the division of stars into constellations, must have happened early. Along with the latter came the observation that five of these stars were not fixed, but changed their positions in a mysterious way. These stars we now call the *planets* Mercury, Venus, Mars, Jupiter and Saturn. All of these planets had a generally eastward motion with respect to the other stars, but sometimes they appeared to slide back in the westward direction for a while and then resume the eastward motion. We now call the eastward motion *direct* and the westward motion *retrograde.* The idea that our earth is a planet is of quite recent origin.

At some stage, men must have begun to wonder what structure of the universe could explain all these motions. What kind of mechanical model could be devised which would account for all the celestial phenomena and which would also predict the future positions of these objects?

1-2   The Geocentric System. Ptolemy

Over the centuries and millenia of time emerged a system that was highly successful in accounting for these observed motions. The keystone of this theory was the belief that the earth was the center of the universe, and at rest—it had no motion through space or rotation on an axis. This lack of motion was accepted because no motion could be felt. The idea of uniform motion of translation or rotation could never be experienced in practice, and it would not be understood until Galileo's pioneering work on force and motion and Newton's later formulation of the laws of motion. Even more simply, it seemed obvious that motion through space would result in a constant wind from the direction in which the earth was traveling. Of course, no such wind was observed.

The geocentric system is often called the *Ptolemaic system* because of the work of Claudius Ptolemy in about A.D. 150. His main contribution was a book called the *Almagest* (the great work) in which he summarized in detail the then-current ideas on the geocentric system. For more than a thousand years after Ptolemy, this system continued to be altered and elaborated. One cannot speak of *the* Ptolemaic system, because it underwent so many revisions. However, it is possible to explain its fundamental features. This we will do in the following sections.

1-3   The Inner Planets: Mercury and Venus

These two planets are morning and evening stars. Venus is seen more often because it is the brighter of the two and is usually seen farther from the sun than Mercury. When one of the planets is east of the sun, it sets after the sun and is an *evening* star. When it is west of the sun, it rises before the sun and is a *morning* star.

According to the geocentric view, both planets were considered to revolve on circles with different centers which were always on a line joining the earth and sun as in Fig. 1-1.

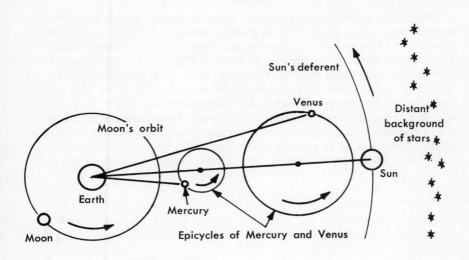

Fig. 1-1. The motions of Mercury, Venus, the moon and the sun in the geocentric system. The view is from above the earth's north pole.

The separate circles for Mercury and Venus are called *epicycles*. Looking from the earth toward the sun in the figure, Venus is seen to the left (east) and is an evening star. In the same figure, Mercury is to the right (west) of the sun and is a morning star. As each planet revolves in its own epicycle in the counterclockwise direction it becomes alternately a morning and an evening star. At any time, the angle planet–earth–sun is called the *elongation*. This angle at its largest is greatest for Venus, and therefore Venus can be seen farther from the sun than Mercury. It is clear that neither planet can be seen opposite the earth from the sun at midnight.

1-4   The Motion of the Moon and the Sun

In the Ptolemaic system the moon revolved about the earth and the explanation of its phases was the same as the modern one. The sun's motion in Fig. 1-1 is counterclockwise (ccw) about the earth in a circular orbit called the *deferent*. As observed from the earth, the sun is seen against a distant background of stars. As it moves in its deferent, its position with respect to the stars will change from day to day, and it will come back to the same place among the stars in one year. Furthermore, the view of the constellations at night will change throughout the seasons.

1-5   The Outer Planets: Mars, Jupiter and Saturn

The outer planets were considered to move around the earth beyond the deferent of the sun. Each of these planets moved in its own epicycle whose center moved on a deferent. Now we can explain the retrograde motion of an outer planet. Consider the case of Mars in Fig. 1-2. The epicycle of Mars moves forward (direct motion, eastward, ccw) with a speed given by the shorter arrow from the epicycle's center. Mars circles this center with a speed given by the longer arrows and is shown in positions *a* and *b*. At *a* the two speeds add together and the motion is eastward. Later, when Mars has made a half revolution in its epicycle to *b*, the speeds will subtract and the motion of the planet will be retrograde (westward, cw). In between *a* and *b* there will be two points where the planet appears to come to rest with respect to the

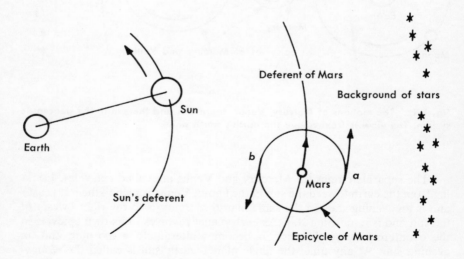

Fig. 1-2.   The epicycle and deferent for Mars to explain retrograde motion of an exterior planet.

stars before it changes its direction of motion. The same explanation applies to Jupiter and Saturn, except that their deferents are larger than those of Mars and the amplitudes of their retrograde motion as seen from the earth are smaller.

1-6   Rising and Setting

In this system, rising and setting must be explained without the rotation of the earth. Therefore, all the motions described must be accompanied by a westward (cw) rotation of the whole sky in a period of one day. Imagine a large circular platform with a central hole where you (representing the earth) stand with your feet on the ground. Around you on the platform move the moon, sun and the planets on circular tracks (the deferents), with you as the center. Around the edge of the circular platform, and attached to it, is a large canvas backdrop studded with stars. The average motion of all the objects with respect to the stars will be to the left (eastward). Standing still and facing in one direction, let the whole platform rotate from left to right and make one revolution in one day. Objects will appear from behind you on your left, pass in front, and disappear behind you on your right. Thus rising and setting are explained for a stationary earth. The entire sky and all objects on it move all the way around and back in one day.

1-7   Comments on the Ptolemaic System

Modern readers are well aware that the earth rotates on its axis and revolves in an orbit around the sun. These sections have been presented to show that for thousands of years man thought otherwise. How was it possible to be so wrong for so long a time? For one thing, there was no evidence that the geocentric system was wrong. Based on the principle that the earth was at rest and centered in the universe, this system was a permissible one. But just as important was the fact that the system *worked*. It did explain the observed celestial motions, and it did so very well. If Ptolemy had been able to use a telescope, he would have observed that Venus and Mercury have phases and that the actual change in appearance of these planets cannot be explained on this system. He would have discovered the satellites of Jupiter, as Galileo did much later, and would have realized that the earth is not the only center of motion in the universe. The insistence on circular motion was based on aesthetic principles, which were not taken lightly by the Greeks. After Ptolemy, later modifications added more epicycles and a variety of other refinements to predict positions more accurately, until the system became cumbersome in the extreme.

Most Greek astronomers did not believe that this description was the actual truth, and only regarded it as a model that worked. But, long after Ptolemy, some medieval astronomers believed so strongly in the reality of epicycles and deferents that finally the system became an article of faith. It is well to realize that in the pre-Christian era, a few astronomers believed the sun to be the center of motion in the solar system, but the intellectual climate of that time was not ripe for such an idea and their views received little attention.

One interesting version of the geocentric system described by Pythagoras (about B.C. 500) had each of the five planets, the sun and the moon carried on separate crystal spheres distinct from the outermost sphere of the stars. The relative motion of these spheres gave rise to the "music of the spheres," which celestial concert could be detected only by the most discerning ear.

The view that the Greeks were pure thinkers and not given to measurement is not correct. Actually a great many celestial measurements were made in the Greek Era. For an interesting discussion of their work, the reader is referred to Abell's *The Exploration of the Universe* as listed in the appendix of suggested readings at the end of this text.

1-8   The Heliocentric, or Copernican, System

This system derives its name from Nicholas Copernicus (1473-1543) who was born in what is now Poland. In the year of his death he published a book which critically examined and compared the geocentric and heliocentric systems. He placed the sun in the center of the solar system, with all the planets revolving about it. As in the geocentric version, he also regarded the moon as the earth's satellite.

He still believed that the orbits were circles and he used epicycles to explain non-uniform orbital motion. In the case of Mars, Copernicus showed that, as seen from the sun, the planet moved with a variable orbital speed. To explain this he had Mars moving in a circular epicycle whose center moved on a circular orbit (deferent) centered on the sun. This is somewhat like the situation discussed in Fig. 1-2 and Sec. 1-5. In this case the speed in the epicycle was less than the speed of forward motion of the epicycle's center on the deferent. Therefore, as Mars revolved in the epicycle its forward motion, with respect to the stars and as seen from the sun, was variable. The retrograde motion of Mars and the exterior planets will be discussed in the next section.

Copernicus did not prove that the sun was the center of the solar system, but he did show that the heliocentric system was a great deal simpler.

1-9   Retrograde Motion, Copernican Style

In this system the retrograde motion of an outer planet is explained as the result of the relative motion of the earth and the outer planet. In Fig. 1-3 the orbits of the earth and Mars are circles centered on the sun. For simplicity the epicycle of Mars as discussed in Sec. 1-8 is omitted. The numbered points on each orbit are equidistant in time and on the orbit. When the earth is at E_1, Mars is at M_1. The spacing of the points on Mars' orbit is smaller because of its lesser orbital motion. After connecting corresponding points on both orbits and continuing the line to the star background, it is seen that Mars moves east (direct) for a while, stops, and then moves west (retrograde) for a time, stops again and begins its normal eastward motion once more. No epicycles are needed to explain the retrograde motion. The

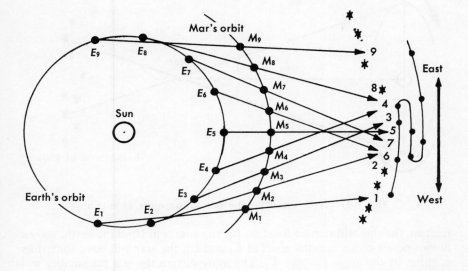

Fig. 1-3.   The retrograde motion of Mars on the heliocentric system.

simplicity of this explanation is one of the strongest arguments for the helio-centric system. The same applies to the motions of Jupiter and Saturn, except that their orbits are larger. The motions of Mercury and Venus are accounted for quite simply by motion in their orbits centered on the sun. The non-uniformity of their orbital motion as seen from the sun required epicycles, as in the case of Mars discussed in the last section.

1-10   Tycho Brahe (1546-1601)

Tycho was one of the most remarkable of all astronomers. Born in Sweden, he was later able to persuade the Danish king to finance an observa-tory on the island of Hven near Copenhagen. He built and used a number of excellent instruments for the determination of planetary and stellar posi-tions with a previously unexcelled accuracy of one minute of arc. During his lifetime he and his wife recorded many thousands of positions, particularly of Mars.

One of his most important contributions was to devise and perform an experiment to distinguish between the correctness of the geocentric and helio-centric systems. In the latter the earth is in orbital motion about the sun. This should result in an annual displacement of nearby stars with respect to the background of more distant stars, as shown in Fig. 1-4. As seen from

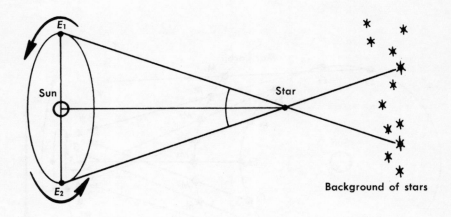

Fig. 1-4. **Tycho's test for the annual parallax of a star.**

the sun, the star will remain fixed during the year, but from the earth, shown in two positions six months apart at E_1 and E_2, the star will have shifted its position by the angle E_1–star–E_2. The more distant the star the smaller will be the angle. Half of this angle, or the angle E–star–sun, is called the *stellar parallax*. If the direction of the star is perpendicular to the plane of the earth's orbit, the parallactic motion will be a circle with respect to the distant star background. If the star is in the plane of the earth's orbit, the shift will be in a straight line. For intermediate positions, the motion will be in the form of an ellipse.

Tycho made this test for a few bright stars which he assumed to be close, but obtained a negative result. Not until 1838 was this done with a positive result, using much more accurate instruments. Tycho failed because his measurements were too crude. For the closest known star the parallax is about three-quarters of a second of arc ($0''.76$). One second of arc is $1/3,600$ of a degree in angular measure. The parallax for the nearest star is some 80 times smaller than any which could be observed by Tycho. With modern telescopes and photographic plates astronomers can measure with confidence a parallax of $0''.02$, $2/100$ of a second of arc. The parallax angle and the distance are related by the formula $p'' = 1/D$, where D is the distance at which the parallax would be one second of arc. This distance has the name *parsec,* and is the technical unit of stellar distance commonly used by astronomers. One parsec equals 206,265 astronomical units or 3.26 light years. As we shall see later, the *astronomical unit* (a.u.) is the average distance of the earth from the sun and is the standard of distances in the solar system. The *light year* is the popular unit of distance, and is the distance that a ray of light will travel in one year (light moves in a vacuum at the rate of approximately 186,000 miles per second). One light year is very nearly 6 trillion miles.

1-11 Johannes Kepler (1571-1630)

Perhaps Tycho's greatest contribution to astronomy was the training of his student Kepler. Kepler began a thorough investigation of planetary motions using the large body of observations obtained by Tycho. He spent most of a 25-year period on the problem and achieved success because he was able to break with the past and discard deferents, epicycles and uniform motion. His justly famous Three Laws of Planetary Motion will now be discussed.

1-12 Kepler's First Law: The Form of the Orbit

Kepler's First Law states: "The form of the orbit of a planet is an ellipse with the sun at one of the foci." To construct an ellipse, place a sheet of paper on a board and drive into the board two nails a short distance apart, as in Fig. 1-5a. Form a knotted string whose total length is a little more, say 20%, than twice the distance between the two nails. Place the loop of string over the nails and draw it tight by means of a pencil tip. Move the pencil all the way around the nails, keeping the loop tight. The resultant curve will be an ellipse and the position of each nail will be one of the *foci* (singular, *focus*). In the same ellipse in Fig. 1-5b the diameter through the two foci will be the *major axis* and from the center of the ellipse to either end will be the *semi-major* axis. The distance *c* divided by the semi-major axis *a* is defined as the

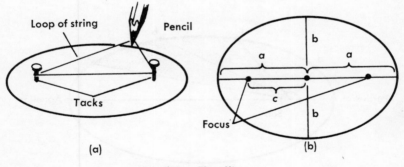

Fig. 1-5. **The ellipse.**

eccentricity (*e*) of the ellipse. Note that for the same length of string the shape of the curve will depend upon the distance between the two nails, and when it is zero the curve will be a circle (constant radius) and the eccentricity will be zero. The semi-minor axis *b* is shown in Fig. 1-5b. When the eccentricity is zero and the ellipse is a circle, *a* and *b* are equal. As the eccentricity increases from zero, *b* decreases with respect to *a*. In the case of a planetary orbit the sun is at one of the foci—there is nothing at the other one. The point where the planet is closest to the sun is called *perihelion*. The most distant point at the other end of the major axis is called *aphelion*. A little algebraic juggling will show that at perihelion the planet's distance is $a(1 - e)$ and $a(1 + e)$ at aphelion.

1-13   Kepler's Second Law: The Law of Areas

Even in the Greek era it was known that the motion of the sun among the stars was not the same at all times of the year, and that this difference accounted for the different lengths of the seasons. To take this non-uniformity into account, a small epicycle was added which moved on the sun's deferent. The new view of Kepler was that the non-uniform motion resulted from the fact that the earth's orbit was an ellipse and that its orbital velocity changed throughout the year. Kepler found that this was particularly true for Mars. This led in time to the Second Law, which states that "the line joining a planet to the sun (the radius vector) sweeps over equal areas in equal intervals of time." This was a brilliant discovery. The meaning of this statement is shown in Fig. 1-6.

Here a, b, c and d are points on the orbit so spaced that the time interval between successive positions is the same, say one year. The Second Law requires that the area bounded by the arc between two successive points and the two radius vectors from the sun to these two points shall be the same for each successive pair of points. This means that when the distance from the sun is relatively large the orbital velocity will be small, so that the area swept out by the radius vector shall be the same as when the distance to the sun is less and the orbital velocity must be larger. Clearly, the orbital velocity will be largest at perihelion and smallest at aphelion.

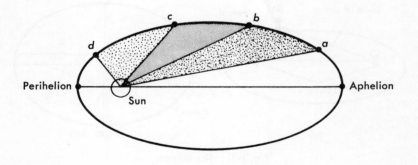

Fig. 1-6.   The law of areas.

1-14   Kepler's Third Law: The Harmonic Law

The Third Law states that "the ratio of the cube of the semimajor axis to the square of the period is the same for all planets." Consider any two planets 1 and 2. The law can be expressed as

$$a_1{}^3/P_1{}^2 = a_2{}^3/P_2{}^2$$

This will be true regardless of the units used. This ratio shows the "harmony" that exists between the planets. This equation can be simplified by using for distances the astronomical unit[1] and for time the earth's orbital period, one year. Let planet 2 be the earth. Then for the earth, $a_2 = 1_{a.u.}$ and $P_2 = 1$ year. Since planet 1 can be any planet, we can drop the subscript and write the formula as

$$a^3/P^2 = 1 \text{ or } a^3_{a.u.} = P^2_{yrs}$$

This formula can be used to find the distance of any planet from the sun in a.u. if the period is known. Later on, Newton was able to derive these three laws from the law of gravity. He showed that a more correct form of the Third Law is as follows:

$$a^3_{a.u.}/P^2_{yrs} = (m_1 + m_2)$$

where the masses are given in the unit of the sun's mass. This form is very nearly the same as Kepler's form, because if m_1 is the sun then $m_1 = 1$ and the mass of a planet (m_2) is much less than one, so that the sum of the masses is very close to unity for all planets. Within the limits of error of his data, Kepler could not have noticed the difference. This latter form of the Third Law will be used many times in succeeding chapters.

1-15 Comments on Kepler's Laws

Kepler discovered these laws by a brilliant analysis of the large body of observations obtained by Tycho. The laws are simple in form, but their importance is very great since they showed that there were laws that governed planetary motions. The introduction of elliptical orbits was a great innovation and an important departure from the ancient idea that all motion must be in a perfect circle. The Second Law is a beautiful and simple description of the change in orbital velocity of a planet. Kepler showed that the Third Law applied not only to the orbits and periods of revolution of the planets but also to the motion of a satellite about a planet. In spite of this tremendous achievement there is something lacking in the laws. They *describe* the motions of the planets and satellites, but they offer no clue to any fundamental explanation based on a law of force. Kepler's laws are magnificent fragments of the greater truth to be discovered some years later by Newton.

1-16 Galileo Galilei (1564-1642)

Galileo, as he usually is called, was one of the greatest thinkers, originators and experimentalists of all time. In his lifetime he advanced the frontiers of science more than any man before him. Galileo's researches in mechanics had a direct bearing on Newton's formulation of the laws of motion.

In 1610 Galileo was the first person who is known to have used a telescope for astronomical observations. With it he discovered the moons of Jupiter, the craters on the moon, star clusters, the phases of Venus and the secret of the Milky Way. He was the first person to study sun spots with a telescope. His discovery of Jupiter's moons showed that the earth was not the only center of motion, as required in the geocentric theory. One of his greatest contributions was his advocacy of the heliocentric system. On this he wrote copiously and with great penetration, and for his views he was resoundingly criticized by the upholders of the older theory which had been raised to the level of theological dogma. The story of this revolt and its eventual success is one of great interest. The reader is referred to the many books on the subject.

1-17   Isaac Newton (1643-1727)

After what has been said about Galileo it would be hard to say more of any other man, except Newton. He is best known for his law of universal gravitation, but, in addition, he contributed a great deal to the study of light and optics and formulated the laws of mechanics. Inherent in these laws is the clarification of the meaning of uniform motion, force and acceleration.

Newton's statement of the law of universal gravitation is that "the force of gravity between any two bodies in the universe is directly proportional to the product of their masses and inversely proportional to the square of the distance between their centers." This rather formidable statement can be expressed in symbolic form as

$$F = G \times \frac{m_1 \times m_2}{d^2}$$

where F is the force, m_1 and m_2 are the masses, and d is their separation. G is called the constant of proportionality. Once the units of mass, distance and force are specified, G tells us the magnitude of the force for given values of the masses and distance. Another way of stating the formula is that the force *depends upon* the product of the masses divided by the square of the distance. Note that the equation says nothing about the temperature, color, physical state or chemical composition of the masses. It is independent of these attributes.

Consider the effect of distance on the force. The fact that d is in the denominator means that the larger the d the smaller the force, but since d is squared it means that the force changes more rapidly than if the first power were used. For example, it says that if we consider the force between the earth and moon as the standard and then double, triple or quadruple the distance, the force will become, respectively, $\frac{1}{4}$, $\frac{1}{9}$ or $\frac{1}{16}$ of the original, standard force. If we cut the distance between the earth and moon to $\frac{1}{2}$ or $\frac{1}{3}$ of its present value the force would become, respectively, 4 times or 9 times larger than its present value. Note that the force only approaches zero as d approaches infinity.

The great importance of the law of gravity is that it expresses the behavior of the force of gravity between any two bodies in the universe regardless of their separation or masses. There is no reason to believe that the law has ever been any different in past time or that it will be altered in any way in the future. One of the most interesting results of the law was Newton's demonstration that Kepler's Three Laws are direct consequences of the law of gravity.

Newton's work marks the end of a very long period of confusion and slow reaching out for an understanding of order and meaning in the universe. After Newton there followed a great host of men who expanded his work and developed that most intricate branch of mathematical physics called celestial mechanics. At long last it was possible to develop in detail the intricacies of the motions of the many bodies in the solar system and to understand all motions anywhere in the universe as they depend on the force of gravity.

QUESTIONS

1. How would the changing pattern of the phases of Venus differ between the heliocentric and geocentric explanations of motions in the solar system?
2. Consider the case of a comet moving around the sun in a very highly eccentric orbit with a period of 10,000 years. Approximately how far from the sun will the comet be at aphelion?
3. Using the data on Mars in Table 4-1, compute the perihelion and aphelion distances of that planet.
4. Draw a series of ellipses under the conditions that (a) the length of the loop of string remains the same but the distance between the nails is changed, and (b), the distance between the nails is fixed and the length of the loop of string is altered.
5. Summarize the arguments in support of the Ptolemaic and Copernican systems.
6. If the distance between the earth and sun were doubled and the mass of the earth tripled, how would the force of gravity of the earth on the sun compare with its present value?
7. Discuss the importance of Kepler's Three Laws of Planetary Motion.
8. What explanation would you give for the fact that Venus is not seen to pass between the earth and the sun at each inferior conjunction.

Chapter 2

The Earth and the Moon

Because the earth is rotating, it is not a sphere but rather an oblate spheroid with an equatorial diameter of 7,927 miles and a polar diameter of 7,900 miles. The mass of the earth is 6.6×10^{21} tons. When this figure is divided by the earth's volume its average density is found to be 5.5 times that of water. Since the average density of the surface rocks is 2.7 times that of water, it appears that some part of the inner regions must have a density higher than the mean value. Seismological and other evidence suggests that the density near the center is 12-15 times that of water.

2-1 The Proofs of the Rotation and Revolution of the Earth

As shown in the first chapter the rotation of the earth gives a simple explanation of the rising and setting of the heavenly bodies. However, the proof had to wait until 1851 when Foucault performed in Paris his famous experiment with the pendulum. To describe this experiment, let us imagine a free swinging pendulum hung from the ceiling of a high room at the earth's north pole and swinging back and forth in a direction toward and away from some mark on a wall of the room. It would soon be observed that the direction of swing was changing and in such a way that the point on the wall marking the direction of swing was moving around the room to the right. Looking down from the ceiling above the point of suspension, one would see that the plane of swing of the pendulum was turning in a clockwise direction. One would obtain the impression that some force was acting on the pendulum bob causing this effect. However, the only force on the pendulum is gravity, which acts vertically downward, and hence cannot influence the direction of the plane of swing. One would be forced to conclude that the pendulum was undisturbed and that the room and the earth were turning under the pendulum in a counterclockwise direction. Since the reference space is the room, the plane of swing will turn in the direction opposite to the rotation of the earth. At the north pole the direction of the swing will come back again to the mark on the wall in one day, or one rotation of the earth. At lower latitudes the period in which the plane of swing turns will lengthen, and at the equator it will not move at all.

The proof of the earth's orbital revolution was obtained quite accident-ally by James Bradley in England in 1727, when he discovered the *aberration of starlight*. Bradley had been trying to detect the parallax of a star (see Sec. 1-11) which passed near his zenith by using a vertical telescope mounted in a chimney, but instead he obtained a much different and much larger effect. The essence of his observations and the proof are as follows. Imagine that it is raining outside, with no wind, so that the drops fall vertically downward. If you stand outside in the rain, holding a pipe, it will be obvious that a rain drop can fall all the way through the pipe and out the bottom only if you hold the pipe vertically as in Fig. 2-1. If you walk at a good pace, a little ex-perience will show that you have to tilt the upper end of the pipe forward by just the correct angle to the vertical so that a drop can enter the upper end and pass out the bottom without striking the inside of the pipe. The angle will depend on how fast you walk and the speed of fall of the rain drop. Let v be the speed at which you are walking and V the speed of fall of the rain drop. If t is the time required for the drop to fall vertically through the tilted pipe, then the vertical distance it falls will be $V \times t$ and the distance by which the upper end of the pipe precedes the lower will be $v \times t$. In mathematical terms the tilt angle A will be given by the tangent of A as the ratio of $v \times t$ to $V \times t$, or v/V. Bradley was observing the ratio of the velocity of the earth in its orbit to the velocity of light. Bradley measured the angle A to be nearly $20''.5$ and thereby demonstrated that the earth was truly in orbital motion about the sun.

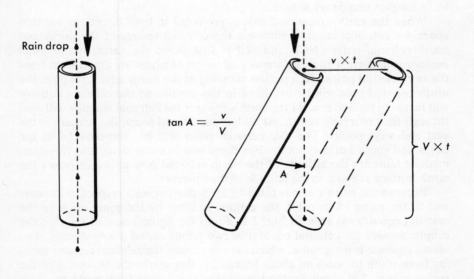

Fig. 2-1. **An analogy to explain stellar aberration.**

2-2   The Orbit of the Earth

The earth's orbit has an eccentricity of 0.017, or $\frac{1}{60}$ (Sec. 1-13). The semi-major axis has a value of 92,900,000 miles, with an uncertainty of about 1000 miles. Because of the eccentricity the earth is closer to the sun by 1.5 million miles in early January and farther from the sun by the same amount in early July than if the orbit were a circle. Because of the law of areas, the orbital velocity is 1.7% greater than the average (18.5 mi/sec) in January and the same amount less in July.

The earth's orbital plane is called the *plane of the ecliptic,* and the path of the sun among the stars as seen from the earth is called the *ecliptic.* The *Zodiac* is that band eight degrees on either side of the ecliptic, and in this band are always found the sun, moon and the planets (with the occasional exception of the moon, Venus and Pluto). The *signs of the Zodiac* are twelve 30-degree divisions along the ecliptic, each with the name of a constellation. These signs are of interest only in astrology but, from the astronomer's point of view, the less said about the subject the better.

2-3   The Celestial Sphere and Celestial Coordinates

The system of longitude and latitude on the earth has its counterpart in the sky. On looking at the sky, day or night, one has the impression of being on the inside of a bowl, the *celestial sphere.* All of the celestial objects appear to be on that imaginary sphere.

When the earth's rotational axis is projected in both directions out into space we can imagine it to intersect the celestial sphere at the *north* and *south celestial poles* (NCP and SCP). Just as on the earth, the *celestial equator* is that great circle on the sky all points of which are equidistant from the two celestial poles. To a person standing at the north terrestrial pole, the north celestial pole will be overhead in the zenith and the celestial equator will lie along his horizon. At the earth's equator the celestial equator will pass through the observer's zenith. At all latitudes it will touch the horizon at the east and west points. The two celestial poles will be, respectively, at the north and south horizon points. For these two extreme cases and for intermediate latitudes the altitude of the north celestial pole above or below the north horizon is equal to the latitude of the observer.

Because the earth's axis is tilted by 23.5 degrees with respect to the normal to the plane of its orbit, the ecliptic is tilted by the same angle to the celestial equator, as seen in Fig. 2-2. From the figure one can see that the ecliptic crosses the celestial equator at two points called the *equinoxes.* The *vernal equinox* is the point at which the sun crosses the celestial equator moving from south to north on about March 21; this marks the beginning of the spring season. On about September 23, the sun moves from north to south across the celestial equator at the *autumnal equinox,* marking the beginning of the fall season. On about June 22, the sun is farthest north of the celestial equator at the point called the *summer solstice* and farthest south on about December 22 at the *winter solstice.* June 22 and September 23 are the be-

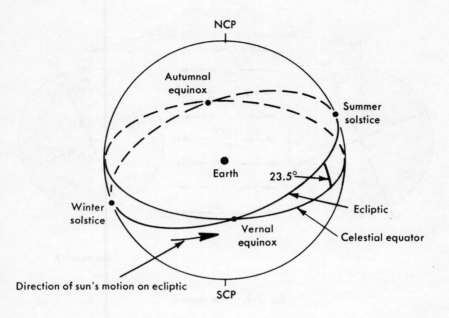

Fig. 2-2.   The celestial sphere.

ginnings, respectively, of the summer and winter seasons. In the sky the astronomer measures the position of a star north or south of the celestial equator in degrees; this position is called the *declination*. Longitude in the sky is called *right ascension* and is measured in hours eastward through 24 hours from the *prime celestial meridian* through the vernal equinox.

2-4   The Seasons

As stated in the last section the earth's axis is tilted by an angle of 23.5 degrees. As the earth revolves about the sun the tilt and the direction of the axis in space remain the same. An exception to this will be considered in the next section. Figure 2-3 represents the appearance of the earth and the direction of the sun's rays on June 22 and December 22. On June 22 the north pole is tilted toward the sun, the south pole is in darkness and it is summer in the northern hemisphere. At this time the daylight period is the longest and the sun attains its maximum noon height in the sky. On December 22 the situation is reversed with respect to the two hemispheres, and it is winter in the northern one. In the northern hemisphere the daylight period is the shortest and the sun at noon is the lowest in the sky. Halfway between these dates, on March 21 and September 23 (the equinoxes), the sun is overhead at the equator at noon and the periods of daylight and darkness are equal. On March 21 the sun is just rising at the north pole for a day of six months

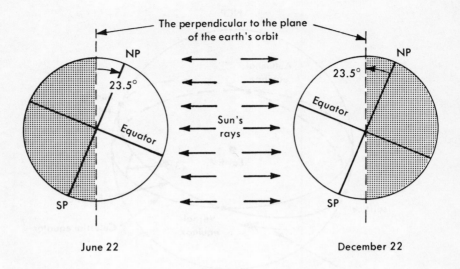

Fig. 2-3. **The seasons.**

and setting at the south pole for a night of the same length. The reverse takes place at the autumnal equinox.

2-5 The Precession of the Equinoxes

Although the tilt of the earth's axis remains essentially constant, the direction does not. The direction of the axis changes continually with time in a period of 25,900 years. This is the phenomenon of *precession*. The axis precesses around the normal to the plane of the earth's orbit, just as a spinning top can be seen to do. This precession is the reaction of the earth to the pull of the sun and the moon on the earth's equatorial bulge. At the present time the earth's axis points in space close to the star Polaris, but it is slowly moving away. About 2700 B.C. the north star was the star Thuban in the constellation Draco. Some 26,000 years from now the pole star will once again be Polaris. Because of precession the equinoxes slide along the ecliptic continuously. Some 2000 years ago the vernal equinox was in the constellation Aries, one of the twelve in the zodiac, but now it has moved westward into Pisces.

The right ascension and the declination of a star are defined with respect to the vernal equinox and the celestial equator. Precession causes this coordinate system to shift with time so that, although the stars remain fixed with respect to one another, the coordinates of all stars are changing continuously. The equinoxes slide along the ecliptic at the rate of nearly one degree every 72 years. The vernal equinox has moved along the ecliptic 25 degrees since the time of Ptolemy.

2-6 Time

The astronomer views time as a rather complex subject, and here only a few remarks will be made on the topic. The basis of all time determinations is the ability to refer our clocks to some time-varying phenomenon which we hope is of constant period for all time. For ages we have used the rotation period of the earth (the *day*) as our standard and have defined the *second* as 1/86,400 part of this period. However, for the last hundred years we have known that the earth is gradually slowing down, with the result that the day is lengthening. The main reason for this is the frictional effect of the ebb and flow of the water tides of the earth. This is particularly effective in shallow bodies of water like the Bering Sea. When astronomers compute the times of occurrence of solar eclipses that took place 2000 years ago they find about a three-hour difference between the observed and computed times.

For most human purposes this longer day matters very little, if at all, but for some astronomical purposes it is most important. The scale of this effect can be understood from the fact that a clock started in 1900 and adjusted continuously to the slowing rate of rotation of the earth would be nearly 35 seconds behind another clock started at the same time and rated to run always at the rotation period of the earth in 1900. At present, astronomers have adopted *ephemeris* time, in which the second is what it was in 1900, as opposed to *universal* time, which uses the instantaneous rate at any time.

THE MOON AND ECLIPSES

2-7 The Moon

The semi-major axis of the moon's orbit around the earth is nearly 239,000 miles, but because of its fairly large eccentricity (0.055, or $\frac{1}{18}$) its distance from the earth is quite variable. Because the moon's orbit is greatly affected by the perturbations of the earth and sun, the eccentricity and other elements are variable, with the result that at its closest point (*perigee*) to the earth the distance may be as small as 221,460 miles and at its farthest point (*apogee*) as much as 252,710 miles. This change in distance produces a very perceptible change in the moon's angular diameter as seen from the earth. The *angular diameter* of an object is the angle between the two lines drawn from opposite sides of the body to the observer's eye.

The distance to the moon has been determined by triangulation measurements from two stations on the earth and also from radar measurements. The error of determination is a little less than one mile. From the moon's distance and its anglar diameter of close to ½ degree, its linear diameter is 2,160 miles. It appears that the diameter pointing toward the earth is about one mile greater than a diameter at right angles. Possibly this is a fossil tidal bulge produced by the earth when the moon was in a somewhat more plastic state than now. The mass of the moon is $\frac{1}{81}$ that of the earth. From this mass and from its volume a mean density of 3.3 times that of water is calculated, a value which is only 60% that of the earth's.

2-8   The Tides

The moon and the sun by their gravitational pull produce the water tides on the earth. Each body produces two tidal bulges, one between the earth and the attracting body and the other on the opposite side of the earth. Each body causes two tidal bulges because the attraction of the body on the water between the earth and the body is greater than the attraction of that body on the earth itself, and the attraction of the body on the earth is greater than the attraction on the water on the side of the earth opposite to that of the body. The tidal bulges due to the moon's gravitational pull are a little more than twice the height of those produced by the sun.

Let us first consider just the lunar (moon) tides and look at Fig. 2-4. First of all, let the moon be fixed in its orbit at M_1. The earth's tidal water is outlined by the solid elliptical curve, with one bulge toward the moon and the other on the opposite side of the earth. The tide is *high* at point a on the earth and also on the opposite side of the earth. Halfway between these two points the water is shallow and the tide is *low*. As the earth turns it carries the water with it, but not the bulges, which remain fixed along the earth-moon line. Under these circumstances there would be a high tide every twelve hours and a low tide halfway in between. However, the moon is mov-

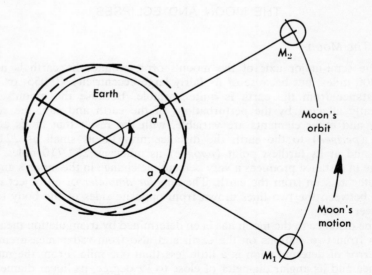

Fig. 2-4.   **The earth tides. The view of the earth is from above the north pole.**

ing forward in its orbit and it carries the tidal bulges along with it. The time interval from the moment when point a is on the earth-moon line with the moon at M_1, until a has made one complete revolution on the earth and a little more and it is again on the earth-moon line at a' with the moon at M_2, is 24^h50^m on the average. At a and a' the tide will be high and there will be another high tide on the opposite side of the earth. Therefore, there will on the average be a high tide every 12^h25^m, with a low tide halfway between each high tide.

The effect of the solar tide is that it may reinforce or partly cancel the lunar tidal range. The tide produced by the sun has an interval of 12 hours between successive solar high tides, but because the latter are somewhat less than half as high as the lunar high tides, the lunar tide predominates and the main effect is that of a high tide of variable height but with an interval of 12^h25^m between high tides. At new moon and full moon, when all three bodies are in the same line, the two sets of tidal bulges reinforce each other and the range of water height is the largest. Such tides are called *spring* tides. At first quarter and last quarter phases of the moon, when the angle moon-earth-sun is 90 degrees, there is a partial cancellation of the tidal range from high to low water and the range in height is the least. This is the time of *neap* tides.

The observed tidal phenomena are much more complex. In the open ocean the spring tidal range is about three feet. Along a coast line the nature of the tides is greatly affected by the slope of the ocean bottom, the shape of the shore line, the latitude of the place and the time of year. In the Bay of Fundy and in bays along the Patagonian Coast the funneling of the water by the bays may cause a tidal range of as much as 50 or 60 feet. It is interesting to note that the pull of the sun and moon produces a tide in the solid part of the earth with a range of about 9 inches. From this observation it can be computed that the earth as a whole has a rigidity about twice that of steel.

2-9 The Phases of the Moon

The moon's phases are the result of the motion of the moon around the earth and the fact that moonlight is reflected sunlight. At *new moon,* in Fig. 2-5 when the moon is nearly between the earth and sun, the illuminated half of the moon is toward the sun and we see no moon. *Full moon* takes place half an orbital period later, a little more than two weeks, and the situation is just the reverse of the one at new moon. At *first quarter* and *last quarter,* halfway between the new and full moon phases, we see only half of the illuminated surface, or one-quarter of the whole moon's surface. For a few days just after and just before new moon, when the moon is in the crescent phase, one can see that the dark portion is faintly illuminated. This illumination is called *earthshine* and it is caused by sunlight reflected from the earth to the moon and back again to the earth. The full moon is about nine times brighter than the quarter moon, even though only twice the illuminated area is seen at the full phase. This is because at first quarter we see many shadows cast by irregularities on the moon, but at full moon the object will hide its own shadow as seen from the earth.

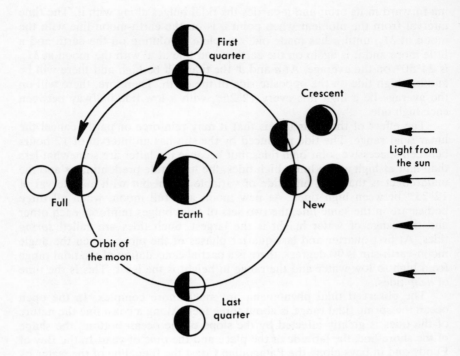

First
quarter

Crescent

Light from
the sun

Full   New
Earth

Orbit of
the moon

Last
quarter

Fig. 2-5. **The phases of the moon. The circles on the moon's orbit are seen from well above the earth looking down on the earth and moon. The outer group of circles represent the view of the moon as seen from the earth.**

2-10   The Temperature of the Moon's Surface

Because the moon rotates once per revolution about the earth, a given surface point is in sunlight for two weeks and in darkness for two weeks. Measurement of the surface temperature in the center of the full moon indicates a value of about 270°F. A little more than two weeks later, at lunar midnight, the temperature has dropped to about −240°F. As a point on the moon enters the earth's shadow during a total lunar eclipse the temperature is observed to drop very quickly. This indicates that the heat conductivity of the lunar surface material is very low and that it is probably of a very porous nature.

2-11   The Face of the Moon

Since the invention of the telescope the surface of the moon has been studied a great deal and its surface has been mapped in detail. Several tens of thousands of features have been charted. Because the periods of revolution and rotation are the same we always see the same side of the moon. Photographs of the other side of the moon were made by the Soviet lunar

Fig. 2-6. The first quarter moon. (Photograph from the Mount Wilson and Palomar Observatories.)

probe in 1959, but because of their lack of clarity not much detail was seen. More recent work by the Soviet astronomers shows much more detail. The surface of the moon is a great complex of mountains, craters, rays, ridges, clefts and plains. Some of the mountains reach heights as great as 26,000 feet. About 30,000 craters have been mapped for the moon. Photographs taken by earthbound telescopes reveal that the crater diameters range from 150 miles down to the optical resolution limit of about 1000 feet. The American Ranger series of spacecraft, with their close-up televised pictures reveal craters, or pits, as small as three feet across. Almost all the lunar craters are circular and some of the larger ones have walls 10,000 feet or more high.

The lunar plains or seas are called by the Latin word *maria* (plural mah-ry'uh; *mare*, singular, mah'ray) because they were once thought to be seas or oceans. However, it has been known for a long time that the moon's surface has neither liquid water nor an appreciable atmosphere. The maria appear to be relatively flat, smooth areas that are quite dark compared to the rest of the moon. Only a few small craters and very few mountains are found in the "seas."

2-12 The Origin of the Moon's Surface Features

To understand the present lunar topographical features it is important to realize that the moon has had no appreciable atmosphere for a few billion years. (See Sec. 4-12 for the problem of the escape of atmospheres.) There-

Fig. 2-7. A lunar crater complex around the crater Clavius. The sunlight comes from the right. (Photograph from the Mount Wilson and Palomar Observatories.)

fore, the erosional processes that are still active on the earth have not been operating on the moon for a long time, and what we see now is a fossil surface.

The majority of astronomers now believe that most of the larger lunar craters were formed by the impact of very large meteoroid bodies a long time ago, when such objects were far more plentiful in the solar system than now. They are now rare probably because most of them have been swept up by the planets. Certainly such craters were formed on the earth at the same time, but erosion has removed almost all vestiges of them. Outside and around many of the larger lunar craters there is ample evidence of debris ejected on the impact explosions. Other points favoring the impact theory are that, at least in the larger craters, the inner crater floor is depressed below the surrounding area outside the crater, and the fact that the craters have a very large ratio of diameter to depth. This is generally contrary to the structure of the earth's volcanic craters. Meteor craters would be explosion craters in which a relatively small body impacting at high velocity on the lunar surface would penetrate to a certain depth and the kinetic energy of the body would be largely used up in blasting out quantities of material. Experience with bomb craters on the earth shows that they are almost always circular and that their shape does not depend on the angle of impact of the bomb. This is not to say that there are no volcanic craters on the moon, but rather that this method of formation has played a minor role.

The lunar mountain ranges were probably formed by the same kind of

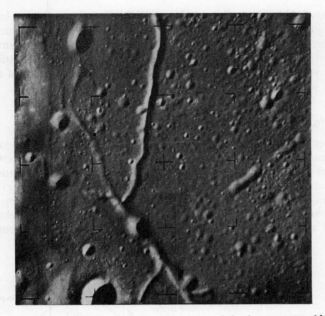

Fig. 2-8. A Ranger IX photograph of the floor of the lunar crater Alphonsus near the crater wall. The photograph shows an area about 8 miles on a side, and the sunlight comes from the right. South is down. Note the long branching group of shallow valleys. (Photograph from the National Aeronautics and Space Administration and the Lunar and Planetary Laboratory of the University of Arizona.)

processes that shape them on the earth. The mountains in the craters may be extinct volcanoes formed shortly after the impact explosion. The maria have the appearance of large lava flows such as the extensive basalt flows seen in the Pacific Northwest. The relative absence of craters in the maria suggests that the maria were formed late in the evolution of the moon, after most of the large meteoroids had been swept out of the interplanetary space. The maria exhibit evidence of extensive faulting, with the formation of long ridges and fault escarpments. The moon's surface may well be covered with a layer of dust consisting of volcanic ash, tiny meteoroids and dust from the impact explosions. The dust may not be loose; probably the particles have been welded together under the vacuum conditions on the moon to produce a fairly spongy mass of the consistency and hardness of pumice.

Although no new lunar features have been discovered since the invention of the telescope, numerous minor disturbances have been seen. One of the most important of these was a Russian astronomer's observation in 1958 of what appeared to be an outburst of gas from a crater. The area brightened, and a spectrogram of the light showed the emission bands of carbon. Since that time at least one other color change has been observed in that area. Recent work suggests rather strongly that some areas of the moon's surface may fluoresce when bombarded by particles of solar origin. If the Russian observation was of gas escaping from the crater, the gas may have been caused to glow by the action of solar ultraviolet radiation or protons of solar origin. This is not to suggest that the phenomenon was the same as the eruption of a terrestrial volcano, although the interior of the moon may still retain some remnant of potential vulcanism. A great many of these uncertainties will be settled when man finally reaches the moon.

2-13   Eclipses of the Sun and the Moon

Eclipses are basically very simple phenomena fraught with a wide variety of complications. The simple explanation of a solar eclipse is that it takes place when the sun, moon and the earth are in the same line, and in that order. A lunar eclipse occurs when the bodies are in the same line, but with the earth in between. Figure 2-9 diagrams some possible situations (clearly it is not to scale). The shadows of the moon and the earth are right circular cones and the apex of each cone is to the right of the body casting the shadow.

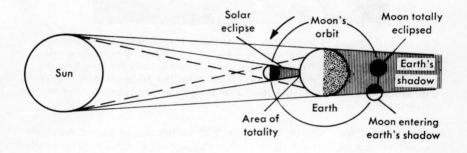

Fig. 2-9.   Diagram to illustrate eclipses of the sun and the moon (not to scale).

In the figure the apex of the moon's shadow (the *umbra*) extends below the surface of the earth, and the intersection of the earth's surface with the dark cone is the region of totality. Under the most favorable conditions the maximum diameter of the region of totality is 167 miles. Since the earth's surface is curved and the moon's distance is variable, it is quite possible that the shadow apex will not touch the earth and the eclipse will not be total. An observer on the shadow's axis but beyond the apex will see an *annular* eclipse, in which the dark circle of the moon is surrounded by a narrow ring of sun. An observer in the region of partial shadow will see a part of the sun and the eclipse will be *partial*. The area on the earth in which the eclipse is partial may easily be several thousands of miles across. Therefore, one's chances of seeing a partial eclipse are far greater than of observing a total one.

For a suitably placed observer the duration of a partial eclipse may be a matter of hours, while the maximum duration of a total eclipse is 7^{m}39^s.

The duration of totality depends mainly on the speed of the moon in its orbit and the rotational speed of the observer on the earth. The moon moves eastward in its orbit at an average speed of 2,100 mi/hr. The maximum eastward rotational speed on the earth is 1,060 mi/hr at the equator. Therefore, the shadow moves eastward at the equator with a speed equal to the difference, or nearly 1,000 mi/hr. At other latitudes the earth's rotational speed is less, the shadow moves more rapidly and the duration of the total phase is shorter. Sometimes it happens that the dark shadow cone misses the earth altogether, so that no total eclipse is seen at all, but only a partial one.

A total eclipse of the moon occurs when the moon moves completely into the earth's dark shadow, whose average length is 860,000 miles. When the moon moves along a diameter of the earth's shadow the duration of the total phase is about 1^h40^m. It is preceded and followed by a partial phase about one hour in length. Sometimes the moon moves so that only a portion of its surface enters the shadow cone of the earth, and then only a partial eclipse is seen. Because of the refraction of sunlight by the earth's atmosphere and absorption in that atmosphere, some light is bent into the shadow and the moon is illuminated by a faint, reddish glow.

2-14   The Importance of Eclipses

Total lunar eclipses are of little scientific interest, except that temperature changes can be measured at these times on the moon's surface.

At one time a total solar eclipse was of the greatest interest because only then could the prominences and the corona be seen. Because it is now possible to produce artificial eclipses at any time, the natural ones are less important. However, astronomers still go to scattered places on the earth to view (weather permitting) total solar eclipses in order to measure the bending of starlight by the gravitational field of the sun, to record the changes in the sun's radio noise during the eclipse and to photograph the chromosphere at the beginning and end of each eclipse. These aspects of the sun will be discussed in a later chapter.

QUESTIONS

1. Strictly speaking, what is referred to as the earth's orbit around the sun is really the orbit of the center of mass of the earth-moon system. How does the observed eastward motion of the sun among the stars compare with what it would be if observed from the center of mass of the earth-moon system?
2. What is the terrestrial longitude of the north pole of the earth?
3. Describe the nature of the earth's seasons under these two hypothetical circumstances: first, the rotational axis is perpendicular to the plane of the earth's orbit; second, the axis lies in the plane of the orbit.
4. How would you expect the tidal range in the open ocean near the north pole of the earth to compare with that in the equatorial regions?
5. How does the eccentricity of the moon's orbit alter the duration of a total eclipse of the sun in the case where the path of totality passes along the earth's equator?

Chapter 3

The Tools and Methods of the Astronomer

Like any other scientist, the astronomer uses a variety of tools and techniques to obtain information and to interpret his data. Since almost all of this information comes in the form of light, it has been necessary to devise a wide range of instruments that will permit a detailed analysis of the light in all its colors and wavelengths. The two most important instruments of the astronomer are the telescope which gathers the light and the spectroscope which analyzes it. Therefore, let us begin with a brief study of light.

3-1 Light

Light is often thought of as that physiological sensation which results in vision and the phenomenon of color. In a broader sense light may be regarded as that form of radiant energy which travels with the speed of light in a vacuum—about 186,000 mi/sec. This broad definition covers such kinds of radiant energy as radio waves, infrared rays, visible light, ultraviolet light, X rays and gamma rays. All of these forms of energy have the same velocity in a vacuum. A more technical term for these several forms of radiant energy is *electromagnetic radiation*. The main difference between these various forms is their wavelength. The accepted unit of wavelength is the *Angstrom* (Å), which is 1/100,000,000 centimeter. The approximate range of wavelengths for visible light is about 4,000 Å for the lower limit of violet light to about 7,500 Å for the longest red rays. The normal human eye has its greatest sensitivity in the yellow-green region at about 5,500 Å. Wavelengths shorter than 4,000 Å are in the ultraviolet (UV) region until one gets down to a few tens of angstroms where the X-ray region begins; at the still shorter wavelengths of less than 1 Å, most of the gamma rays are found. Waves longer than 7,500 Å are in the infrared region, a very broad one, up to about one centimeter (100,000,000 Å). At about this limit begins the radio region, where wavelengths are given in centimeters or meters. None of these regions is sharply bounded.

3-2   Reflection, Refraction, and Dispersion

In Fig. 3-1 consider a narrow beam of light consisting of the two colors violet and red. Let this beam in air strike a flat glass plate at some angle, not zero, with respect to the perpendicular (normal). As seen in the figure, three things will take place. First, a part of the incident beam will be reflected from the air-glass interface. The law of reflection is that the angle of incidence i equals the angle of reflection i', and that the normal is contained in the plane of the incident and reflected rays. This is true for all colors.

The second effect is that after entering the glass the direction of the beam will be changed in such a way that it is bent toward the normal. This is *refraction*. The third effect is *dispersion*, which means that the violet light will be bent more than the red. The angle of refraction r is less for the violet light. Intermediate values of r will be found for the other colors between violet and red. The angle of refraction depends upon the angle of incidence and the *index of refraction n*. The latter is the ratio of the velocity of light in a vacuum to the velocity in some transparent medium such as air, glass or water. The index is always greater than unity. For any transparent medium, n will increase as the wavelength decreases. The variation of n with wavelength will be different for each different medium.

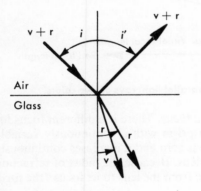

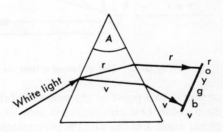

Fig. 3-1.   Reflection, refraction and dispersion.

Fig. 3-2.   The Prism and the spectrum.

3-3   The Prism and the Spectrum

Consider a beam of white light (all colors) which strikes a prism with a prism angle A as in Fig. 3-2. As the light enters the glass it will be split up into a ray for each component color or wavelength (only two are shown in the figure). A further bending will occur when the rays leave the prism. If a white card is placed in the emergent, dispersed beam a spectrum will be seen. A *spectrum* is a display, or analysis, of the component colors, or wave-lengths, in the original beam. Very commonly the spectrum is photographed for detailed study, but other instruments such as various types of photo-electric cells are also used. The spectrum of a source usually extends into the ultraviolet and infrared regions and these are studied in the same way.

3-4   Lenses

With the above background we are now in a position to understand the action of lenses. Almost always the surface of a lens is either flat (plane) or a section of a sphere. Figure 3-3 shows the action of a double convex lens on parallel light rays that are parallel to the lens axis and are of two colors, say violet and red. It is clear from the figure that after the parallel rays from the left pass into the lens and emerge on the right, they are refracted and

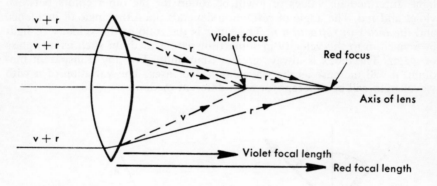

Fig. 3-3.   **The action of a lens on parallel light rays of two colors.**

converge to a point on the axis called the *focus*. There is a different focus for each color. One can regard a lens as a prism with a continuously variable prism angle. On the axis the prism angle is zero and it increases continuously to its maximum value at the edge of the lens. Because the index of refraction for violet light is the greater, the distance from the lens to its focus (the *focal length*) is less than for red light.

3-5   Lens Aberrations

Before considering image formation by lenses it would be well to com-ment on the fact that the lens in Fig. 3-3 does not have the same focus for violet and red light. The other colors have intermediate foci. This effect is called *chromatic aberration* and it is one of the several faults, or aberrations, of lenses. The ideal lens would bring all the rays to the same focus. Other aberrations not to be discussed here have names such as spherical aberration, astigmatism, coma, etc. For their study the student is referred to a text on geometrical optics. It is not possible to eliminate all aberrations completely, but by a proper lens design and the use of more than one lens in the system one can reduce all of them to minimum values. Chromatic aberration can be greatly reduced by a combination of two lenses of different kinds of glass. Most astronomical refracting (lens) telescopes have an objective consisting of a double convex lens of one kind of glass and a plano-concave lens of another kind.

3-6 Image Formation by Lenses

Consider the double convex lens in Fig. 3-4 and neglect any aberrations. Imagine that the parallel rays coming from the left are from an object as distant as the moon, so that the rays from any one point are practically parallel. The rays from a point on the moon that is on the axis of the lens are brought to a focus on the lens axis. Those rays from a point above the

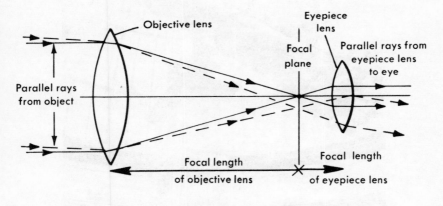

Fig. 3-4. **Image formation and the eyepiece.**

axis (dashed rays) will be brought to another focus below the first one and at the same distance from the lens. Each point on the moon (or any other object) will be imaged at its own focus and, ideally, all these foci will be in the same *focal plane*. Note that the image will be inverted with respect to the object. As long as the rays from the object are sensibly parallel, then all images of all objects regardless of distance will be in the same focal plane.

If the lens were that of a camera a photographic film or plate would be placed in the focal plane. However, if the lens is the objective of a visual telescope an eyepiece is placed to the right of the focal plane in such a position that the focus of the eyepiece is in the focal plane of the objective. The rays from each point of the image will emerge from the eyepiece as parallel rays and pass into the eye, where another image will be formed on the retina by the eye lens. The magnification m will be given by F/f, where F is the focal length of the objective and f the focal length of the eyepiece. To change the magnification, eyepieces of different focal lengths are used.

The arrangement just described is the one used in an astronomical re-fracting telescope. The inverted image produced is not objectionable to the astronomer—when such an arrangement is used in a terrestrial telescope or field glass it is necessary to introduce an *erecting* lens or prism. The telescope in Fig. 3-5 is the world's largest astronomical refractor. The objective lens has a focal length of 63 feet and a diameter of 40 inches. The rotating dome is 90 feet in diameter and is equipped with a shutter that may be opened for observing. The observing floor is 75 feet in diameter and can be moved vertically through a distance of 35 feet, so that the observer may always sit on a chair whether he is looking at an object in the zenith or low on the horizon.

Fig. 3-5. **The forty-inch refracting telescope of the Yerkes Observatory of the University of Chicago. (Photograph from the Yerkes Observatory.)**

3-7   The Reflecting Telescope

One good way to completely eliminate chromatic aberration is to use a mirror telescope, as described in Fig. 3-6. Let parallel rays from the left strike a mirror whose surface is a section of a sphere, and let the center of curvature be the point c on the mirror axis. Observe that the innermost and outermost sets of rays are not reflected to the same focus. For a set of rays very close to the axis, the focal point will be halfway between the center of curvature and the mirror surface. For parallel rays farther from the axis, the focus will be at points progressively closer to the mirror. This effect is called *spherical aberration*. To bring all rays to the point $c/2$ it is only necessary to increase in a smooth and particular way the radius of curvature of the zones farther from the axis. The resulting cross section is not a circle

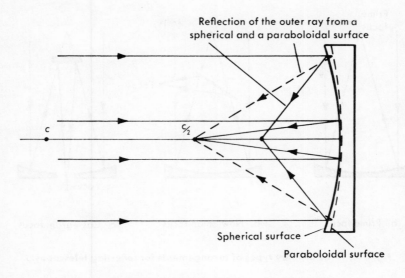

Reflection of the outer ray from a
spherical and a paraboloidal surface

c

c/2

Spherical surface

Paraboloidal surface

Fig. 3-6. **Reflection from a spherical and from a paraboloidal surface.**

but a *parabola,* and the mirror surface is a paraboloid of revolution about its axis. The dashed curve is the parabolic one.

3-8   *The Types of Reflecting Telescopes*

In the reflecting telescope the large primary mirror is placed at the bottom of a supporting tube and the mirror focus (the prime focus) is at some point in the tube on the axis, as in Fig. 3-7a. In a large telescope one can place a plate camera at the prime focus; for a few large reflectors, such as the 200-inch Hale Telescope, a cage for the observer is placed in the tube. The cage obstructs some of the light but does not spoil the image formation. For smaller telescopes, where one might wish to use an eyepiece, a flat mirror is placed in the tube before the focus so that the focal plane is brought outside the tube. This is the Newtonian form, as shown in Fig. 3-7b. The third standard form is the Cassegrain type (Fig. 3-7c). Before the light reaches the prime focus, it is intercepted by a hyperbolic mirror which reflects the light back down the tube through a hole in the mirror to a point behind the mirror. This form is a convenient one to use, since the focus is always closer to the observing floor than it is in the Newtonian form.

3-9   *Refracting and Reflecting Telescopes Contrasted*

The primary reason for using a telescope is to gather light and to increase the brightness of an object with respect to what it would be to the naked eye alone. Magnification is usually a secondary consideration, but it is not unim-

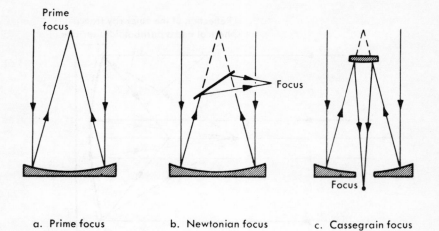

a. Prime focus   b. Newtonian focus   c. Cassegrain focus

Fig. 3-7.   **The primary types of arrangements for reflecting telescopes.**

Fig. 3-8.   **The 200-inch Hale telescope of the Mount Palomar Observatory. (Photograph from the Mount Wilson and Palomar Observatories.)**

portant. For many years almost all observations have been made using photography. Visual inspection is sometimes necessary and even superior to the photographic record, as in observations of Mars. But the great advantage of a photographic record is that it is permanent and the photographic plate contains far more information than can be gathered by the eye and remembered by the brain. Visual studies must be made at the telescope at the time of observation, but a photographic plate can be examined later on and preserved for the use of future generations of astronomers.

The larger the telescope objective the more light is gathered. Fainter objects can be detected and brighter ones can be photographed in a shorter time. It is difficult to obtain large lenses for a refracting telescope that are free of defects such as inhomogeneities in the glass and small bubbles. For a two-element refractor, four surfaces must be polished and figured to the correct curve. For a reflector there is only one surface to be figured and the glass need not be transparent. Most lenses absorb the ultraviolet part of the spectrum below about 3,400 Å, and large parts of the infrared region. For a glass mirror coated with aluminum the range of the reflected spectrum is far greater.

Since the glass of a mirror need not be transparent, large thick mirrors can be made that will not bend (show flexure). A lens can be supported only around its edges, but a mirror will have a system of edge and back supports. Mirrors are usually made of a glass such as Pyrex, whose dimensions change less for a given temperature change than ordinary glass. This is quite important because in the early part of a clear night the temperature drop is often large. An ordinary glass mirror would loose its figure until the temperature had been stabilized; a pyrex mirror would be much less affected, and one of fused quartz would show hardly any change of shape.

The first telescope mirrors made by Newton and William Herschel in England in the late 17th century and in the 18th century were made of a metal which could be given a high polish but which tarnished rather easily and lost reflectivity. When the tarnish was removed the mirror had to be refigured, a long and tedious job. Toward the end of the 19th century mirrors began to be made of glass, and a chemically deposited coat of silver became the reflecting surface. When the silver tarnished it could easily be removed with chemicals (which did not affect the glass) and be replaced with a fresh silver coat. However, silver tarnishes rather easily when sulfur fumes from burning coal are present in the air. In the 1930's silver was replaced by a vacuum evaporated coating of aluminum. This metal is not as soft as silver and it is much more resistant to corrosion. Its reflectivity is high in the ultraviolet, where that of silver is not. A coating of aluminum may last for years, while the lifetime of a silver coat may be only a few months.

It should be remarked in conclusion that a considerable amount of research is now in progress on better materials for the body of the mirror itself and on new engineering designs for the mounting. The main trouble with all kinds of glasses is that they are poor conductors of heat; hence, as the night air becomes cooler, the outer parts of the mirror shrink faster than the inner portion. The result is a warping of the figure alluded to in an earlier paragraph. Experimental materials are now available that do not change their dimensions with change of temperature, but it remains to be seen if they are suitable for use as mirrors. One new material is aluminum itself. It is a good conductor of heat and it is stronger than glass, so that the body of the mirror need not be as thick as glass must be to prevent flexure. For one such mirror of aluminum, now under construction at the Kitt Peak National Observatory near Tucson, Arizona, the aluminum mirror surface is covered with a non-corrosive material, which of itself is not a good reflector. This surface is then figured to the correct parabolic curve and a thin reflecting coating of aluminum is evaporated on the non-corrosive layer. As for telescope size, there are plans for instruments much larger than the 200-inch Hale telescope. It is clear that in order to support the mirror and prevent flexure in it and the tube and mounting, new engineering designs will be necessary. Such studies are now in progress.

3-10   Resolution

For every optical system there is an absolute upper limit to the amount of detail that it can reveal in a given object, regardless of the amount of magnification. This limitation is exemplified in the inability of a given telescope to detect lunar features below a certain size or to reveal the duplicity of a double star at less than a given angular separation. The basic cause is the finite wavelength of light, and the explanation is one that the student must seek in a text on physical optics. Resolution is usually expressed as the minimum angle of separation as viewed by the telescope. This angle is made smaller (and the resolution higher) the larger the telescope aperture and the shorter the wavelength. Wavelength is not important for visual telescopes since the wavelength range is small, having an average value of 5,500 Å. The complete formula for the minimum angle of resolution is given by $\theta = 1.22$ λ/d, where θ (the Greek letter *theta*) is expressed in radians, λ (the Greek letter *lambda*) is the wavelength in centimeters and d is the aperture in centimeters. A more convenient form for visual telescopes using the average wavelength of 5,500 Å is given as $\theta = 4''.5/d$, where θ is given in seconds of arc and d in inches. From this formula we see that for the 40-inch refractor of the Yerkes Observatory (Fig. 3-5) the minimum angle of resolution is about $0''.1$ and for the 200-inch Hale telescope it would be about $0''.02$.

In practice the latter resolution will seldom if ever be realized because the light must pass through the earth's atmosphere. This causes tremors and enlargements of the image so that on a night of poor "seeing" the minimum angle of resolution may be much larger than the theoretical formula would predict for that telescope. It is for this reason that astronomers spend much time in site surveys to locate places where the meteorological conditions will minimize poor seeing. Another difficulty with the earth's atmosphere is that it is not transparent at all wavelengths. The main "window" which includes the visible region extends from about 2,900 Å to roughly 12,000 Å. Below 2,900 Å the atmosphere is completely opaque at all wavelengths. About 12,000 Å there are long stretches of opaque regions interspersed with occasional windows in this extensive infrared region. The absorption below 2,900 Å is due mainly to oxygen and ozone molecules. Above 12,000 Å the main contributors are water vapor and carbon dioxide. Spectra of Mars and Venus have been obtained with considerable success in the infrared by using large balloons to carry spectrographs to an altitude of 80,000 feet; at this elevation the instrument is above 90% of the earth's atmosphere. The sun's ultraviolet spectrum has been studied by instruments carried in rockets to altitudes well above most of the earth's atmosphere. An even more ambitious project is the Orbiting Astronomical Observatory (OAO), which is intended to place a 30-inch telescope in orbit around the earth at an altitude of about 250 miles. The amount of atmosphere above this altitude is negligible as far as absorption goes. The telescope in this satellite will be remotely controlled from ground stations and will have the capability of being pointed toward any desired object. Under these conditions it will be possible to study the spectra of celestial objects in any wavelength region to which the instruments are sensitive. Although this capability will be a great boon to astronomers, the cost of an OAO is so great that for many years most observational work in astronomy will be done at ground based observatories.

SPECTROSCOPY

Spectroscopy is the science and art of the analysis of light by means of a study of the light's component wavelengths (the spectrum). Astronomical spectroscopy is a highly sophisticated field and its study has revealed an enormous amount of information about our solar system and the stars beyond.

3-11   The Spectroscope

The spectrum is produced by a *spectroscope,* a simple form of which is shown in Fig. 3-9. The light from the telescope enters a narrow slit on the left. The diverging rays from the slit are intercepted by a collimator lens and made parallel after which they pass through the prism and are dispersed. The camera lens focuses the dispersed rays on a photographic plate. This instrument is called a *spectroscope* when the spectrum is observed visually and a *spectrograph* when the spectrum is photographed. If the slit is illuminated by light of only one wavelength an image of the slit is produced at the appropriate place in the spectrum. This image is called a *spectral line* and it is an image of the slit in monochromatic light.

THE THREE TYPES OF SPECTRA

3-12   The Continuous Spectrum

Fortunately all of the kinds of spectra may be reduced to three classes, even though they may and often do occur in combination in astronomical cases. The first of these types is the *continuous spectrum,* which consists of all wavelengths. This type is emitted by any hot solid or any hot or glowing

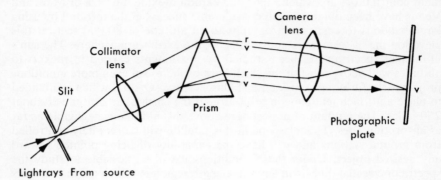

Fig. 3-9. **A simple spectroscope showing the formation of two separate spectral lines, one each for a wavelength in the red and the violet.**

gas under high pressure, regardless of its chemical composition. To the eye, the appearance of the visual region is a continuous band of color from violet through red, although the ultraviolet and infrared wavelengths are also present. Two examples of sources emitting a continuous spectrum are the hot tungsten filament of a light bulb and the hot, high pressure gases of the sun's photosphere.

The only difference between the continuous spectra from various sources depends upon the source temperature. In Fig. 3-10 are plotted the spectral energy distributions for the sun $(5750°K)$ and for two other sources, one much hotter and the other much cooler. The symbol K refers to temperatures measured on the *absolute* scale, on which the zero point is absolute zero. The K symbol is a tribute to Lord Kelvin, an English physicist who made many theoretical contributions to the meaning of absolute zero. On the absolute scale (or Kelvin scale) $0°K$ is $-273°$ C (centigrade) and the degree divisions are the same as those of the centigrade scale. The Kelvin scale will be used commonly in our later discussion of stellar temperatures. The theoretical curves for each temperature are called *black body radiation* curves, for reasons which are beyond the scope of this text. Along the vertical axis are expressed energy units per unit area per unit time. An example might be calories (or ergs) per square centimeter per second. The energy is zero at zero wavelength. For any temperature, as the wavelength increases from zero, the energy rises to a maximum and then decreases and approaches zero again as the wavelength approaches infinity. It can be shown that the total energy in all wavelengths (the total area under the curve) increases as the fourth power of the absolute temperature, and also that the wavelength of the maximum varies inversely as the first power of the absolute temperature.

Note the part of each curve which lies in the visible region between the two dashed vertical lines. For the cooler body there is more red than blue-violet light and therefore its color will be predominantly red. For the hotter body there is more blue-violet than red light and its color will be on the blue

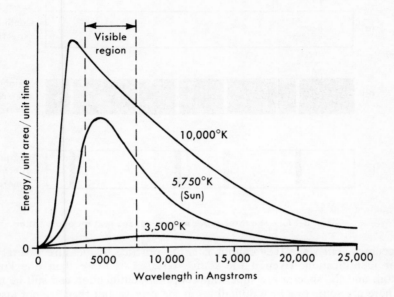

Fig. 3-10. The spectral energy distribution curves for the sun and for two other bodies, one hotter and the other cooler.

side. For the sun's curve there are about equal amounts of radiation from either end of the visible region, so that the resulting color is close to white or perhaps a little on the yellow side. We shall have many occasions to refer to these curves again.

3-13   The Bright Line Spectrum

This second type of spectrum is emitted by any hot or glowing gas under *low* pressure. The spectrum from any such source is characterized by a group of spectral lines, each of a very narrow range of wavelength or color. There is no light between the lines—the spaces are dark. Figure 3-11b shows the bright line spectrum in the visible region of mercury vapor under low pressure. The important feature of this kind of spectrum is that every chemical element and each of its possible stages of ionization has its own characteristic bright line spectrum. No two are alike. None of the wavelengths are the same. Therefore, the bright line spectrum of an atom becomes its "finger print" and serves to indicate its presence in the source. After a great deal of labor by spectroscopists the bright line spectra of all of the chemical elements and of many of their ionized states have been obtained; the wavelengths have been measured and are available in the literature. In theory only one line needs to be measured to identify the chemical element from which it comes. This would be true if wavelengths could be measured with infinite

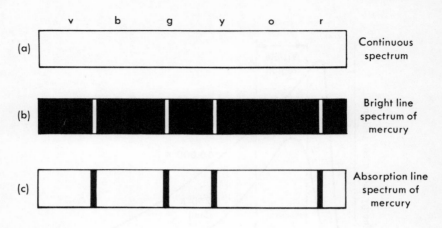

Fig. 3-11. **The three types of spectra. See text for explanation.**

accuracy, but since they cannot it is the practice to measure several lines for identification. Even if the source consists of more than one kind of atom and the spectra are superimposed, the identification can still be made. There are some practical difficulties in the process but they are not insuperable.

3-14   The Absorption Spectrum

This kind of spectrum occurs because, in general and in an elementary way, each low pressure gas tends to absorb just those wavelengths which it can emit as a bright line spectrum. The production of an absorption spectrum can be understood by reference to Fig. 3-12. Assume that the source of light produces a continuous spectrum, that is, all wavelengths. The absorption tube just in front of the slit has transparent ends and sides. With no gas in the tube the spectrum will be continuous, as in Fig. 3-11a. Now fill the absorption tube with low pressure mercury vapor. The appearance of the spectrum will be that in Fig. 3-11c. The wavelengths of the dark absorption lines are the same as those of the bright lines. It thus appears that mercury vapor acts as a filter, in the sense that it is opaque to the light of the wavelengths of the bright lines and transparent to all others. Therefore, the absorption spectrum of an element will also serve to identify the element.

When the atoms in the tube absorb certain wavelengths the energy removed from the beam is stored up in the atoms, but quickly released. The direction in which the light is released is at random with respect to the direction from which the light came from the continuous source, so that only a very little is reradiated toward the slit. Now, if one were to point another spectroscope toward the side of the absorption tube, the bright line spectrum of mercury would be seen. The mercury vapor in the tube absorbs just those wavelengths which it would radiate as a low pressure gas. If all the

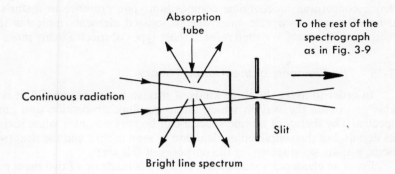

Fig. 3-12. **The production of an absorption spectrum.**

reradiated energy continued on through the slit, there would be no absorption lines. The manner of formation of the absorption spectrum of mercury applies to any other gas at low pressures.

The production of an absorption spectrum in the laboratory is usually not as simple as indicated here, but in principle the description is correct. Some gases absorb at room temperatures and others only at elevated temperatures.

Another matter of interest is that molecules may also absorb, and each kind of molecule has its own characteristic absorption spectrum. Most molecular absorption is in the infrared region. Molecules in our atmosphere such as oxygen, nitrogen, carbon dioxide and water vapor (particularly the latter two) absorb fairly large quantities of the infrared radiation of the sun and contribute strongly to the temperature of the earth's atmosphere. However, the opacity of the atmosphere below 2,900 Å is due largely to the absorption of ozone and oxygen.

Usually molecules do not produce a bright line spectrum when excitation is produced by heating unless the atoms in the molecule are tightly bound together. For those in which the interatomic forces are weak the elevated temperatures cause the molecules to break down into molecular fragments or into individual atoms. Examples of molecular emission are found in the spectra of comets, where the excitation is due not to heat but to the excitation produced by ultraviolet rays and energetic protons from the sun. For the same reasons, absorption spectra of molecules in stellar spectra are seen only in the cooler stars. In the sun this phenomenon is observed only in the cooler, central regions of sun spots and only for molecules that are tightly bound, like titanium oxide.

An understanding of these laws of spectra is very important to the astronomer. A determination of the shape of the spectral energy distribution curve for a star will lead to a determination of its temperature. The identification of the wavelengths of the absorption or emission lines will reveal which elements are present. The absorption spectrum of a planet's atmosphere will give evidence concerning its chemical composition. The presence in a star's spectrum of many absorption lines due to ionized elements indicates that its temperature is high. We shall refer to these types of spectra many more times.

3-15   The Elements of the Atomic Theory

In order to make the three kinds of spectra more meaningful, it is desirable to discuss the way in which atoms produce absorption and emission spectra. The theory of atomic spectra can be very complex when seen in all its details, but the simplified explanation as seen in this, and the next two sections, is quite satisfactory for the purposes of this text.

From an elementary standpoint, an atom is made up of two main parts: a nucleus with a positive electrical charge and a cloud of negatively charged electrons that swarm around the nucleus. The central nucleus is about ten thousand times smaller than the whole atom and it is made up of two kinds of particles called *protons* and *neutrons*. The proton is a positively charged particle but the neutron has no electrical charge. Their masses are nearly the same and each has a mass about 1800 times greater than that of one electron. The quantity (or strength) of the electric charge on a proton and an electron is the same but their signs are opposite.

All of the atoms of a particular chemical element have the same number of protons in the nucleus. Except in the simplest form of hydrogen, all nuclei have neutrons, but their number does not concern us in this discussion. There are no electrons in the nucleus. In a *neutral* atom, the total amount of positive electrical charge in the nucleus is exactly balanced by the total amount of negative charge on the electrons. This means that in a neutral atom the numbers of protons and electrons will be equal. It is relatively a difficult matter to remove a proton from a nucleus but rather easy to strip an electron from an atom. The process by which an electron is removed is called *ionization*. When one electron is removed, the atom is said to be singly ionized; doubly ionized when two are removed; and so on, for higher states of ionization. Atoms can be ionized by the collision of high speed atoms in a hot gas; by bombarding the atoms with energetically moving electrons from outside; or by exposing the atoms to sufficiently energetic light radiation. The latter method will be discussed later on.

The simplest of all atoms are those hydrogen atoms in which there is one proton in the nucleus and one electron revolving about the nucleus. The next, more complicated atom, is helium, whose nucleus contains two protons (and some neutrons) around which revolve two electrons. The most complicated atom found in nature (not artificially produced in the laboratory) is uranium, whose nucleus contains 92 protons which are matched by a cloud of 92 electrons. In a simple way, one may regard an atom as a kind of solar system in which the massive nucleus is the sun and the electrons correspond to the planets. However, because an atom is a submicroscopic particle, it is not possible to actually *see* what it looks like; but one can make models of the atom which are designed to represent their observed behavior.

3-16 A More Extended View of the Nature of Light

In Sec. 3-1, it was stated that light may be regarded as a wave motion much like water waves. This idea is perfectly satisfactory in explaining a wide range of phenomena, among which are reflection and refraction (Sec. 3-2); but a variety of effects, involving the interaction of light with atoms, cannot be explained by the wave theory. About A.D. 1900, there arose a new theory—the quantum theory (quantum from the Latin for quantity)—which clarified these earlier observations. The theory states that a beam of light is not a succession of waves but rather is a stream of particles of energy all moving with the speed of light. These particles are sometimes called quanta (plural of quantum), but a more commonly used term is *photons*. In the wave theory, one regards the light energy from a source as consisting of a continuous stream of waves such as those produced when a rock is tossed into a quiet pool of water, and the water waves radiate from the impact point in concentric circles. In the quantum (photon) theory, the light energy proceeds in all directions from the source (such as the filament of a light bulb) as a random stream of individual particles of light energy. An imperfect, but reasonably accurate comparison, is given by the case of a lawn sprinkler which sprays the grass with individual water drops.

The amount of energy contained in a photon depends, in a simple way, on the wavelength of the light. It may seem odd to speak of the wavelength of a photon, but it is convenient to do so, in order to relate the quantum and wave theories of light. The relation is given by the formula $E = C/\lambda$, where E is the photon's energy, λ the wavelength of the light, and C is a constant whose value depends on the units used for energy and wavelength. In our discussion, we need not be concerned about the units, but only to realize that since λ is in the denominator of the fraction, the larger the wavelength of an individual photon, the smaller will be its energy and, conversely, the smaller the wavelength, the larger and more energetic will be the photon. Therefore, if we were to proceed to smaller wavelengths in going from infrared to red to violet and on to shorter wavelengths in the ultraviolet and x-ray regions, the photon energy would increase.

To reply to the question concerning which is the correct theory of light—the wave or the quantum theory—the answer is that both are correct but that each has its own appropriate use.

3-17 Energy Levels in Atoms. The Absorption and Emission of Light by Atoms

After the discussion of the last two sections, we are now in a position to consider the mechanism by which atoms absorb and emit light. To do this, we shall consider, in some detail, a model of the simplest of all atoms—the hydrogen atom. As was said in section 3-15, this atom is made up of a nucleus with a single proton around which revolves a single electron in what may be regarded as a circular orbit.

Imagine for the moment that it is possible for the electron to move in an orbit of any radius. Remember that because the electrical charges of the proton and the electron are of opposite sign, there is an attraction between them. As a start, let the electron be moving in a small orbit close to the nucleus, and then, by some means, it is moved into a larger orbit. Because of the attractive force between proton and electron, it is necessary to oppose this force when the electron is moved into a larger orbit. Work must be done on the electron, and energy must be given to the atom as a whole. As a result, the electron will have more energy of position in a large orbit than in a smaller one. A reasonable analogy is that of a person walking up a ramp. On going from the bottom to the top of the ramp, he is in a higher state of energy of position because work was done in increasing the person's distance from the center of the earth against the gravitational attraction of the earth on the person.

It had been discovered, through experiment and mathematical studies, that the electron cannot exist in an orbit of just *any* radius. In a simple way, the size of the orbits are restricted by the formula $r_n = r_1 \times n^2$, where r_1 is the radius of the smallest permitted orbit, and r_n is the radius of the *n*th orbit, where $n = 1, 2, 3$, etc. up to any value of n, although there are practical limits. The electron energy is the lowest in the first orbit and increases by distinct steps as it is raised to higher orbits. One may say that there exists for the electron—or for the atom as a whole—a series of energy levels where E_1 is the energy of the lowest orbit, E_2 for the second orbit, and so on. When the electron has the energy E_1 it is said to be in the *ground state,* and in higher levels it is said to be in *excited* states. The diagrams in Fig. 3-13 are an illustration of the energy levels for hydrogen. The vertical scale is in order of increasing energy upward. Observe that, as one goes upward, the energy difference between successive levels decreases. The convergence is such that the energy does not increase indefinitely but finally reaches a level $E\infty$ (read: E infinity) beyond which there are no definite levels. The energy $E\infty$ corresponds to that of an electron orbit whose n approaches infinity. One must realize that the orbit cannot be infinitely large, but only that n reaches some very large value. For practical purposes, the orbit radius cannot be larger than the distance between the atoms in a gas. For our purposes, this distance is great enough so that by the standards of the hydrogen atom it is essentially infinitely large. E_∞ is the energy required to remove, completely, the electron from the hydrogen atom; that is, to *ionize* it. All of the possible energy differences between states have different values—none are identical.

We are now in a position to understand the absorption and emission of light by the hydrogen atom. Let us start with the electron in the ground state E_1. If the electron is to be raised to the second orbit, or second state of energy E_2, one must supply (to the atom) the energy equal to the difference $E_2 - E_1$. One way to do this is to have the atom absorb a photon having just this amount of energy. If the photon energy were just a little bit less (or a little more) than $E_2 - E_1$, the atom would ignore the photon and it would not be absorbed. If the photon energy is increased to $E_3 - E_1$, the atom would again absorb the photon and the electron would jump from the first to the third orbit. The point of this is that for hydrogen atoms in the ground

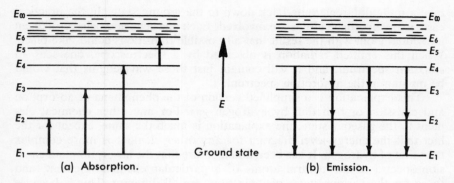

Fig. 3-13. **The energy-level diagram for the hydrogen atom.**

state the gas is transparent to all photons except those with the energies $E_2 - E_1, E_3 - E_1, E_4 - E_1$, etc. The electron has no place to go and can have no existence between the orbits corresponding to this series of energy levels.

When the electron is in one of the excited states, it will remain there for about one one-hundred-millionth of a second and then drop back to the ground state. If, while it is in an excited state, the atom receives a photon whose energy corresponds to the difference between that state and some higher state, the electron will jump to the higher energy state, or level. In Fig. 3-13(a) are shown jumps from the ground state to E_2, E_3, and E_4, and also a transition from E_4 to E_6.

In Sec. 3-15 it was seen that the relation between energy and wavelength for a photon is $E = C/\lambda$. By inversion, the formula becomes $\lambda = C/E$. The wavelength of a photon that causes the transition from the ground state to E_2 would be $C/E_2 - E_1$ and, similarly, for any other energy difference. The result is that if light from a continuous source of radiation were to pass through hydrogen, the consequent spectrum would show absorption lines at just those wavelengths corresponding to photons whose energies were equal to all of the possible energy differences in the energy-level scheme of hydrogen.

Now consider the case of a hydrogen atom in some excited state whose electron is not to be raised to some higher level. After its short lifetime in that level, it will leave and cascade back down to the ground state. As it cascades down, it becames *de-excited* and can arrive at the ground state in different ways depending on the level from which it starts. Let the electron be in E_4, and see Fig. 3-13(b). It could make one large jump all the way down to the ground state and emit a photon with energy $E_4 - E_1$. The other possibilities are E_4 to E_3, E_3 to E_2, and, finally, E_2 to E_1 with the emission of three successive photons whose energies would be, respectively, $E_4 - E_3$, $E_3 - E_2$ and $E_2 - E_1$. Further possibilities are E_4 to E_3 and E_3 to E_1, or E_4 to E_2 and E_2 to E_1. If the atom started at some higher state than E_4, the possibilities become more numerous. Quite naturally, one atom can only exhibit one pattern at a time. If it were excited back to the same state again, it might well take a quite different route back down to the ground state. In the practical case, many hydrogen atoms are involved. Each one acts, and behaves like, an individual atom with the result that all possible transitions could take place. When this emitted radiation is observed by a spectroscope, one sees an *emission* spectrum, and it will contain just those wavelengths that would be missing in the absorption spectrum.

This explanation is a simplified version of the phenomena of absorption and emission of radiation by hydrogen gas. For any other chemical element in the gaseous state, the explanation is much the same, except for the fact that the energy-level diagram for any other element is more complex than that of hydrogen. It has been noted before that the absorption and emission spectra of the neutral atoms of a particular chemical element, and those for the various states of ionization, are all different. This is because their energy-level arrangements are different. As a consequence, it is possible to tell from the appearance of the spectrum what the various stages of ionization in the gas may be.

Brief mention should be made here of the emission of a continuous spectrum by a hot gas under high pressure or a hot solid. In both cases, the atoms are so close together that they disturb each other to an exteme extent with the result that the normal energy levels are each broadened to the point where they overlap and the well defined energy levels no longer exist. The result is that the normal set of definite levels is broadened out into a continuous band containing, in effect, an infinite number of levels. Therefore, transitions of all energy sizes can take place and all wavelengths will be present to form a continuous spectrum.

3-18   The Doppler Effect. Radial Velocity

When one listens to a tuning fork vibrating with a frequency, for example, of 250 vibrations per second, a note of that pitch (frequency) is detected by the ear. In effect, the ear counts the number of sound waves that reach it per second and the sensation of pitch is produced. In air at normal temperatures sound travels at about 1000 feet per second. In a train of waves 1000 feet long there will be 250 waves and hence the wavelength will be about 4 feet. Therefore, the wavelength is equal to the velocity of sound, v, divided by the frequency, f, or $\lambda = v/f$ or $f = v/\lambda$.

When one hears the siren of an approaching fire engine he hears a certain pitch of the siren until the engine passes, and then the pitch suddenly drops. Neither pitch is the true frequency of the siren. This change in frequency results from the relative motion of the source and the observer is called the *Doppler effect*. An observer moving toward a stationary source will detect more waves per second than if he were at rest, and the frequency will be higher. An observer moving away from a stationary source will detect fewer waves per second because the waves must overtake him, and the frequency will be lower.

When the observer is at rest and the source is in motion the result is the same, but the explanation is a little different. A source at rest emits circular sound waves centered on the source, and the number emitted per second is equal to the frequency. When the source is moving it still emits circular wave fronts, each one centered at the point where the source was located when the particular wave was emitted. Because the source is in motion, the wave fronts will be closer together on the side toward which the source is moving and farther apart in the opposite direction. Therefore, as the source moves toward the observer at rest, the observer will hear a higher frequency than the normal one and vice versa when the source is moving away.

Light behaves in much the same way. Light frequency is higher than the rest (or laboratory) frequency when an observer and a source of light are approaching each other, and lower when the two are receding from each other. As a rule the astronomer deals in wavelengths and not frequencies. From the formula stated in the first paragraph of this section, it can be seen that wavelengths are longer than the laboratory values when the source and observer are receding from each other, but shorter when they are approaching. The wavelengths of all the absorption (or emission) lines of a receding star will become longer and they will be shifted toward the red end of the spectrum. The reverse is true for velocities of approach. If the laboratory wavelengths are known (usually this is no problem) the shift can be measured and the velocity obtained from

$$v = \frac{\Delta\lambda}{\lambda} \times c$$

where λ is the laboratory wavelength of the spectral line, $\Delta\lambda$ (read: delta lambda) the wavelength shift for this line, and c the velocity of light. As an example, suppose the laboratory wavelength to be 5,000 Å, the shift toward the red (plus) to be 1 Å, and the velocity of light 186,000 miles per second. Substituting these values in this formula, one can see that the velocity is one of recession by the amount of 1/5,000 of 186,000 miles per second, or 37.2 miles per second. Note that it is not possible to tell whether the star or the earth is in motion, or if both are moving. This is as it should be: there is no such concept as a body being at rest, except as one chooses a particular moving frame of reference. For any given star, as many spectral lines are measured as possible and the mean of the calculated individual line velocities is taken. The velocity obtained in this way is called the *radial velocity* since only motion in the line of sight, or along the radius, can be detected by this means. It is a powerful tool.

3-19 Radio Telescopes

The newest and perhaps the most exciting field in astronomy is radio astronomy. The subject will be discussed in later chapters, but here some mention will be made of radio telescopes as instruments. Some of these telescopes look like gigantic bed springs. Others are a cross with each arm a half-mile or more long, but most of them resemble vastly oversized optical telescopes.

Most radio telescopes are large for two reasons. First, the larger the surface area the more radio energy it collects and, therefore, the stronger the

Fig. 3-14.   **The twin 90-foot diameter radio telescopes of the Owens Valley Observatory of the California Institute of Technology. (Photograph from the California Institute Technology.)**

signal. The second reason involves the characteristic of resolution discussed in Sec. 3-10. The radio waves studied have wavelengths ranging from about one centimeter to many meters. The equation for the minimum angle of resolution in Sec. 3-10 can be rewritten as $\theta = 69.9\ \lambda/d$, where θ is in degrees and λ and d are in centimeters. One wavelength that is studied a great deal is the 21-cm (about 8-in.) radiation from neutral atomic hydrogen in interstellar space. For a radio telescope with a diameter of 50 meters (155 ft) the resolution is not quite 0.3 degrees. This value is vastly larger than the optical resolution for even a medium sized optical telescope, but then the wavelength used here is much larger (2.1 billion Å). High resolution is needed to obtain accurate positions for radio sources in the sky, to separate those that are close together and to determine the structure of a source if its area is large.

The largest radio telescope in the world is 1,000 feet in diameter and is located in Puerto Rico. The largest fully steerable instrument is 250 feet in diameter and is located near the University of Manchester in England. The largest meridian radio telescope is 300 feet in diameter and is at the National Radio Astronomy Observatory at Green Bank, West Virginia.

A radio telescope does not take a photograph. It measures the intensity of the radio waves coming from that part of the sky limited by the resolution of the instrument, as defined by the diameter of the instrument and the wavelength at which it is working. Some of the largest radio telescopes have been used as radar instruments in studies of the planets and the sun.

QUESTIONS

1. What would be the advantages to observing the sun, moon, planets and stars with a telescope placed in an orbit around the earth above our atmosphere?

2. How could you determine the value of the astronomical unit in miles by making radial velocity observations of a star that lies in the plane of the earth's orbit?

3. What is the magnification of a telescope if the focal lengths of the objective and eyepiece are, respectively, 38 feet and ¼ inch?

4. Compare the relative merits of refracting and reflecting telescopes.

5. What would be the required diameter of the objective of a telescope that could just resolve the two components of a double star whose separation was 0″.3?

6. What are some of the practical values of a knowledge of spectroscopy for industrial applications?

7. Consider the problems in building a telescope much larger than the 200-inch Hale reflector.

8. At what places in their orbits relative to the earth would you expect the radial velocities of the planets to be zero?

Chapter 4

Planets and Satellites; Comets and Meteors

The solar system is a variegated assemblage of bodies extending many billions of miles in all directions from the sun. Were it not for the gravitational grip of the sun, all would be chaos, and in a short time the present system would be dispersed into space and anonymity. In this system there are nine known planets, 31 satellites, thousands of asteroids, many thousands of comets, uncounted numbers of meteoroids, great quantities of interplanetary dust and gas and the sun. The total solid volume of all this material is but a minute fraction of the space included in the solar system. One is left with the impression of a vast emptiness in which he might occasionally chance upon some tiny particle such as a planet.

4-1 The Scale of the Solar System

No one, not even an astronomer, is capable of visualizing the enormous distances in the solar system. They are mere numbers. Nevertheless, some idea of the scale can be formed by imagining the sun with its diameter of 864,000 miles to be reduced to the diameter of a one-foot basketball. With all dimensions reduced on this scale, the earth would be a BB shot 109 feet from the sun. Jupiter would be a Ping-pong ball 570 feet from the sun. Pluto, our most distant planet, would be smaller than the earth and 4,300 feet from the sun. The distance to the nearest known star would be 5,700 miles.

4-2 Measuring Distances in the Solar System

Solar system distances such as the sizes of orbits and the diameters of objects are measured by a variety of means. Basically it amounts to measuring the distance in miles from the earth to the sun. Some of the methods are quite complex, but here an attempt will be made to give the reader a feeling for the methods and to discuss a few methods in a simple way.

Let us remember Kepler's Third Law, which states that $a^3 = P^2$, where a is in astronomical units and P in years (Sec. 1-15). It is clear that if the period of revolution is known for a body revolving around the sun, one can use the formula for a determination of its semi-major axis in astronomical units. Let us consider the earth, where *a* is one a.u. and *P* is one year, and another planet whose period has been determined to be 1.1 years. Assume circular orbits for both planets. Squaring 1.1 and then taking the cube root of the result shows that the planet's orbit has a radius *a* of about 1.066 a.u. In other words, when this planet is closest to the earth its distance is 0.066 a.u. But how many miles is this? This would be easy to determine if you knew that 1 a.u. $=$ 93,000,000 miles (round numbers), but suppose you did not know that. Then you would have to measure by some means the distance of the planet at closest approach. This can be done by triangulation from the earth. Let us imagine that at closest approach the planet is observed from two widely separated stations on the earth and the angular difference in direction of the planet, as seen from each station, is measured with respect to the background of the stars. One can easily calculate (from the known positions of the two stations) the distance from one to the other *through* the earth; then it is a matter of simple geometry to determine the distance of the planet at the time of observation. Suppose that this distance turned out to be 6.14 million miles—this would be equal to 0.066 astronomical unit. From this, we would deduce that one a.u. is about 93 million miles. In this simple way, we have determined the value of the astronomical unit.

If the orbits were elliptical and not in the same plane, the problem would be more complicated in practice but not in principle. In principle all that needs to be done is to compute at any time the separation of the earth and the planet in astronomical units and then measure that distance in miles by triangulation from the earth. Since the displacement of the planet with respect to the stars will be small, it is desirable to use a nearby planet so that the displacement is as large as possible and the percentage error of measurement is as small as possible. For this purpose, astronomers like to discover asteroids (Sec. 4-11) that come close to the earth.

Another method using this technique is that of measuring the distance to the planet by radar. A powerful beam of radar waves is beamed at the planet and one measures the time required for the feeble, reflected signal to return to the earth. One half of this time, multiplied by the velocity of light, gives the distance to the body. (By this method, a value of the astronomical unit has been obtained.) This has been done several times for Venus and the results appear to be superior to the older triangulation method. Other methods that have been used in the past will not be described here. The measurement of the astronomical unit in miles is a fundamental astronomical problem.

4-3 The Two Solar Families

Even a casual inspection of the solar system reveals that, except for the sun, all of its members fall into two distinct families—the family of the planets and asteroids, and the family of the comets and meteors. Without exception, all of the members of the first family revolve about the sun in direct (ccw) motion. The average orbital eccentricity is low as compared to that of the second family. Among the planets, Pluto has the highest orbital eccentricity (0.25), and a few of the asteroids have even higher values. The average orbital inclination with respect to the plane of the earth's orbit is small, with Pluto again having the largest value (17 degrees). With the exception of Uranus, all of the planets apparently rotate ccw on their axes. There is now some evidence that the rotation of Venus is cw, but it remains to be confirmed. The direction is unknown for Pluto. Table 4-1 gives some data on the planets and the largest asteroid, Ceres.

In the second family, the comets and meteoroids, the situation is quite different. The average orbital eccentricity is much higher and it may range from nearly zero to almost unity. The orbital inclination can range from zero to as much as 90 degrees and the direction of revolution is often retrograde (cw). This classification strongly suggests that the two families have quite different origins.

Table 4-1.   Planetary Data.

Planet	Mean Distance from Sun (millions of miles)	(a.u.)	Orbital Period	Orbital Eccentricity	Inclination to Ecliptic (degrees)	Mean Diameter (miles)	Mass (earth =1)	Density (water =1)	Rotation Period
Mercury	36	0.39	88^d	0.206	7.0	2900	0.05	6.1	88^d
Venus	67	0.72	225^d	0.007	3.4	7600	0.81	5.06	?
Earth	93	1.00	365^{d}¼	0.017	0.0	7913	1.00	5.52	23^{h}56^m
Mars	142	1.52	687^d	0.093	1.8	4200	0.11	4.12	24^{h}37^m
Ceres	257	2.77	4.6^y	0.077	10.6	488	0.0001	?	?
Jupiter	483	5.20	11.9^y	0.048	1.3	86,800	318.4	1.35	9^{h}50^m
Saturn	886	9.54	29.5^y	0.056	2.5	71,500	95.3	0.71	10^{h}14^m
Uranus	1,783	19.18	84.0^y	0.047	0.8	29,400	14.5	1.56	10^{h}45^m
Neptune	2,794	30.06	164.8^y	0.009	1.8	28,000	17.2	2.29	15.7^h
Pluto	3,670	39.52	248.4^y	0.249	17.2	3,600?	0.1?	?	6.4^d

4-4   *The Aspects of the Planets. Mercury and Venus. The Inferior Planets*

As explained in Fig. 4-1, both Mercury and Venus may be seen as either morning or evening stars. Looking from the north side of the orbit and from the earth, the planet at $P(E)$ is east of the sun and sets after the sun as an *evening* star. At $P(M)$ the planet is west of the sun and rises before the sun in the morning as a *morning* star. At these two positions the planet is also farthest from the sun as seen from the earth. These are the positions of greatest *elongation,* east or west, where the sun-earth-planet angle is the elongation.

Both of these planets show phases. At *superior conjunction* (SC) the earth, sun and the planet are in line and the whole illuminated disc is seen,

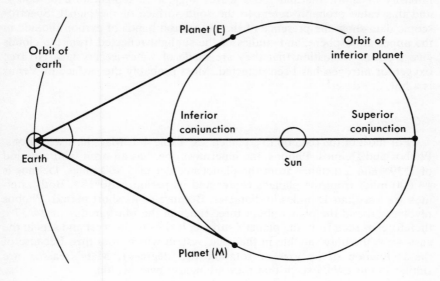

Fig. 4-1. **The aspects of an inferior planet.**

but the image is small because of the planet's relatively great distance from the earth. At *inferior conjunction* (IC) the view is of the dark side of the planet. At $P(E)$ and $P(M)$ the planet is at quarter phase. When Venus is a short distance on either side of IC it shows a large, narrow crescent of great brilliance. At IC there may be relatively rare occasions when either planet passes directly across the sun's disc and a *transit* of the planet occurs. The fact that this does not happen at each inferior conjunction is due to the inclination of the orbit of each planet with respect to that of the earth.

4-5 The Physical Nature of Mercury and Venus

Mercury moves quickly around the sun in a rather elliptical orbit (see Table 4-1). For a long time it was thought that Mercury always kept the same face toward the sun, so that rotation and revolution were synchronous. Some radar data now suggest that this is not so, but the data have not yet been confirmed. Mercury's rotation rate must be slow, because the side toward the sun has a temperature in excess of 600°F. A few surface markings can be seen and it may have a very thin atmosphere.

The surface of Venus is covered by a very thick cloud layer. No permanent markings have ever been seen. Recent unconfirmed radar data suggest that rotation and revolution are not synchronous and that the rotation may be retrograde. Measurement of the heat radiation from the planet shows that the bright and dark sides have nearly the same upper cloud surface temperature of −35°F. This suggests either a mixing of the atmosphere from one side to the other or a fairly rapid rotation, or both. The intensity of short, thermal radio waves suggests a temperature of 600°F and this value probably refers to the solid surface of the planet. Spectroscopic data show the presence of the absorption bands of carbon dioxide in the upper atmosphere, and studies of the sunlight reflected from the clouds give a strong indication that they are made of water-ice crystals. No free oxygen or nitrogen has been detected. Most probably the surface of Venus is a hot, dry desert.

4-6   Mars

For most of the data on this planet, see Table 4-1. Mars has two moons, Phobos and Deimos. Phobos, the innermost one, has an orbit with a period of 7^h39^m and a distance from the planet's center of 5,800 miles. Deimos is 14,600 miles from the planet's center and its period is 30^h18^m. Both satellites are less than 15 miles in diameter. Because of its short period, Phobos revolves around the planet about three times in the Martian day of 24^h37^m; therefore, as seen from the planet's surface, it rises in the west and sets in the east—it is the only satellite in the solar system which does this. Because of the inclination of its axis of rotation (25 degrees), Mars' seasons are similar to our own, except that they are nearly twice as long.

4-7   The Telescopic Appearance of Mars

Even at its closest approach of 35 million miles, the angular diameter of Mars is only 25″. Using a 40-inch telescope with an angular resolution of 0″.1, one could see detail on the planet 1/250 of its linear radius of 4,200 miles, or about 17 miles. Detail smaller than this could not be seen with a 40-inch telescope under atmospheric conditions which would allow the use of the limiting resolution of that telescope. At only a few known sites in the world can this be done with reasonable frequency. Under average atmospheric conditions (the view of) Mars is a disappointing one. The planet's color is reddish, and large dark and light areas are readily visible. When it is winter in one hemisphere, a large, white polar cap can be seen; this cap comes and goes with the seasons. Under the very best observing conditions, it is sometimes possible to see parts of the surface covered by a network of fine lines.

4-8   The Atmosphere and Temperature of Mars

Infrared photographs of Mars show the larger surface features quite clearly, but those taken in violet light are much less distinct and often show no features at all except a polar cap. This is evidence for a Martian atmosphere because blue light is scattered and diffused by gas molecules and dust to a much greater extent than infrared light, with the result that in blue light the surface details are blurred. See Fig. 4-2. Other evidence for an atmosphere is the clouds that occasionally are seen. The blue and white clouds are probably made of ice crystals, like a frozen fog. The yellow ones, since they are seen to move across the surface, are probably dust clouds.

Mars (Sept. 11) and San José as photographed from Mt. Hamilton, (a) and (c) with violet, (b) and (d) with infrared light. The obliteration in (c) is due to the earth's atmosphere, and the comparison is suggestive of the presence of an atmosphere of considerable density on Mars. San José is distant 13½ miles.

Fig. 4-2. Photographs of Mars in violet and infrared light. (Photographs from the Lick Observatory.)

By means of the spectroscope, it is not hard to detect the absorption spectrum of carbon dioxide in the Martian atmosphere, and more recently a very small amount of water vapor has been observed. Neither oxygen nor nitrogen has been detected. The main difficulty in the determination of the chemical composition of the Martian atmosphere is that all these gases are also present in the earth's atmosphere. The sunlight that is absorbed by these gases passes twice through the Martian atmosphere and once through our own before it reaches the slit of the spectrograph. To detect the additional absorption produced by Mars, one can compare the absorption spectrum of Mars with that obtained by looking directly at the sun or the moon. In the latter cases, only the absorption in our atmosphere is observed. The difference then is due to the Martian atmosphere alone. Another technique is to observe the spectrum of Mars when it is either approaching or receding from the earth with a large radial velocity. Under these conditions, the absorption spectrum of the constituents of the Martian atmosphere show an appreciable Doppler shift with respect to the spectral lines produced in our atmosphere.

This latter technique was used to reveal the presence of water in the Martian atmosphere.

Surface temperature values are obtained by measuring the heat radiation from the planet's surface and filtering out the reflected radiation from the sun. The results show that the maximum equatorial temperatures are about 80°F around noon and down to −100°F just before dawn of the next morning. The dark areas seem to be about 15°F warmer than the lighter ones. Such large diurnal temperature changes are not found on the earth because our heavier atmosphere prevents much of the infrared radiation from leaving the earth at night, and hence the cooling rate is retarded. Apparently the Martian atmosphere is so thin that this "blanket effect" is nearly absent.

It appears then that the Martian atmosphere is very thin as compared to that of the earth. In summation, one can say that the most prevalent gas is carbon dioxide, that water vapor is present in very small amounts and that neither oxygen nor nitrogen has been detected. Estimates of the atmospheric pressure at the surface of Mars show that it must be less than one-tenth that at the earth's surface, or equivalent to that found on the earth at an altitude of about 100,000 feet.

4-9   Life on Mars

The spirited discussion of the possibility of life on Mars began in 1877 with Schiaparelli's discovery of the fuzzy network of lines which later came to be regarded as a network of canals that brought melted, polar ice water to the dry equatorial deserts. Clearly, if the canals are real, they must have been built by intelligent life with considerable engineering skill. However, the existence of this kind of life on Mars is extremely doubtful. The fact that the polar caps reflect infrared radiation in the same way as snow suggests that they are frozen water and not dry ice (frozen carbon dioxide). The spectroscopic evidence of little water vapor in the atmosphere means that the surface is very dry. The disappearance of the polar cap in summer shows that the ice layer is very thin. The reality of the system of lines discovered by Schiaparelli is unknown, but it is certain that they are not canals. The low atmopsheric surface pressure, the large diurnal temperature changes, the apparent lack of oxygen and the small amount of water all conspire against any forms of life on that planet anywhere nearly as highly developed as our own. Seasonal color changes in the dark areas suggest vegetation, but spectroscopic evidence rules out chlorophyll. It is still possible that there are low forms of life on the planet, exisiting precariously.

4-10   The Recent Mariner IV Observations of Mars

In November 1964, the United States launched the space vehicle Mariner IV on a mission to Mars. The vehicle passed Mars on July 14, 1965, at a distance of a few thousand miles from the surface. During the time of closest approach, 21 photographs were taken of the planet by television techniques and radioed back to the earth. The most startling features revealed in the photographs were about 70 craters from 3 to 75 miles across, looking much like those on the moon. From the area covered in the photographs it is estimated that there may be as many as 10,000 craters on Mars. We have already seen that Mars has a thin atmosphere; the presence of the craters suggests strongly that it has been thin for a long time, as it has on our moon. Measurements made by the satellite give independent confirmation that the atmosphere is very thin. It was also shown that Mars has no detectable magnetic field. This information was somewhat unexpected since it had been assumed that the inner structure of Mars is much like that of the earth.

4-11 Bode's Law. The Asteroids

In 1772 the German astronomer Bode called attention to an interesting numerical progression relating the distances of the planets from the sun to their numerical order. Write down the numbers 0, 3, 6, 12 and so on, doubling the number each time. To each of these numbers add 4 and divide the sum by ten. Reference to Table 4-1 will show that these numbers give rather closely the distances in astronomical units of the planets Mercury through Saturn, the last one being the most distant planet known in Bode's time. However, there was no planet at 2.8 a.u. as there should have been if the progression was to have meaning.

On the first night of the 19th century, Piazzi in Italy discovered a relatively faint object which moved on succeeding nights. It was soon shown to be a planet revolving about the sun at 2.8 a.u., in seeming confirmation of Bode's law. As time went on, the even more startling discovery was made that many more of these objects exist in the gap between Mars and Jupiter, and that their average semi-major axis is close to 2.8 a.u. Does this imply that Bode's law is some kind of fundamental relation? The extension of the relation beyond Saturn predicts the distance of Uranus rather well but not that of Neptune or Pluto. It is probable that the law is no more than an interesting relation of a coincidental nature.

4-12 The Asteroids

The objects just mentioned are most often called *asteroids*. By now several thousand have been discovered. The majority have semi-major axes between 2.3 and 3.3 a.u., averaging close to 2.8 a.u. All revolve in direct motion and most have small orbital inclinations. Their orbital periods range from about 3.4 to 6 years. On the whole, the orbital eccentricities are like those of the planets, but a few have values so large that at closest approach to the sun they are inside the earth's orbit.

Ceres, the first asteroid to be discovered (and the largest), has a diameter of 480 miles. The observable asteroids have diameters as small as about one mile. These small diameters are obtained from the brightness of the reflected sunlight and an estimate of the reflectivity of the asteroid's surface. The fact that many show periodic fluctuations in brightness must mean that their shape is irregular. It has been estimated that the total number of asteroids may be several tens of thousands and that their combined mass cannot be greater than about 1/1000 the earth's mass. Their origin is unknown but their irregular shape suggests either that they are fragments of a broken planet or that they resulted from the collision of two small planets.

4-13   The Escape of Atmospheres

We have seen that Venus and the earth have substantial atmospheres and that Mercury's is rather scanty. Our moon appears to have none, Mars' atmosphere is thinner than that of the earth and later on we will learn that those of the major planets Jupiter, Saturn, Uranus and Neptune are very dense and thick. To understand this situation, we shall have to consider what is meant by the *velocity of escape* and the velocity distribution of the molecules in a gas.

Neglecting atmospheric friction, the velocity of escape from a planet's surface is that velocity with which a body would have to be projected from the surface in order that its velocity would approach zero as its distance approached infinity. Clearly the body would never return—its orbital period with respect to the planet would be infinitely great. This escape velocity depends upon the square root of the ratio of the mass of the planet divided by its radius. (The greater the pull of gravity at the planet's surface, the larger will be the escape velocity.) In miles per second, the value for a number of objects is: earth (7.0), our moon (1.5), Mercury (2.6), Venus (6.2) and Jupiter (35).

In any gas, the average velocity of the molecules is directly proportional to the absolute temperature of the gas. If the number of molecules at each velocity is plotted as a function of velocity, it is seen that the number at zero velocity is zero. As the velocity increases, the number of molecules increases to a maximum, and then tapers off toward larger velocities so that at larger and larger velocities the numbers of molecules become progressively smaller. Further, at any given temperature the average velocity decreases as the mass of the molecule increases. In the earth's atmosphere at about 300° K, the average velocity of the oxygen molecules is about $\frac{1}{3}$ mi/sec, but for hydrogen it is four times greater at the same temperature.

Now it ought to be clear that for a molecule to escape from the earth's atmosphere it must have a velocity of at least 7 mi/sec. Escape would be possible only in the high atmosphere where both the density and the chance of collision are small. Since the average value is only ⅓ mi/sec—much less than the escape velocity—the fraction of all molecules with velocities in excess of the escape value would be extremely small, although not negligible. The important thing to remember is that only that fraction of molecules with velocities greater than the escape value is potentially able to escape. In an atmosphere consisting of equal numbers of molecules of hydrogen, water, nitrogen, oxygen and carbon dioxide (in increasing order of molecular weight), the hydrogen would escape most rapidly because it would have the highest average molecular velocity; carbon dioxide would escape least rapidly. The result would be a gradual fractionation of the atmosphere, so that after a long time little hydrogen would remain and most of the carbon dioxide would have been left behind.

It is now possible to see why the earth and the moon have such different atmospheres: the moon's escape velocity is much less than the earth's. Mercury has a poor atmosphere because of its relatively low escape velocity and high temperature, both of which increase the escape rate. Mars has an intermediate atmosphere, but note that heavy carbon dioxide is the most abundant gas. Fractionation seems to have operated here. The situation on Venus is not far different from that on the earth. As we shall see shortly, Jupiter has a very heavy atmosphere which contains much light hydrogen in addition to heavier molecules. Both its high escape velocity and its low surface temperature retard escape. The same factors affect the atmospheres of Saturn, Uranus and Neptune. One must not assume that the factors discussed in this section are the only ones that determine the amount of a planet's atmosphere at the present time, but they certainly contribute to our understanding of the nature of planetary atmospheres.

THE GIANT PLANETS

Mercury, Venus, Earth and Mars are all of nearly the same diameter and very much smaller than Jupiter, Saturn, Uranus and Neptune. Pluto, too, is much smaller, but some astronomers regard it as an escaped satellite of Neptune and not as an original planet. The first four planets have densities not much lower than our earth's and all are probably rocky objects. The next four planets are all much more massive, but their mean densities are considerably lower. It has been suggested that each of these planets consists of a large core of solidified hydrogen and helium which is surrounded by a high density atmosphere. Spectroscopic studies of their atmospheres show the absorption spectra of hydrogen, ammonia and methane. Of all the planets, Jupiter is the most massive, with about 1/1000 the sun's mass; its mass is equal to that of all the other planets combined.

4-14 Jupiter

Jupiter is truly the king of the planets. Its diameter and mass are the largest and yet its mean density is only 1.35 times that of water. With the telescope, one observes dark and light bands parallel to the planet's equator. These must be cloud features and not solid surface markings because the band widths may change with time and the rotation period is not the same for all bands. Another feature of the apparent surface is the Great Red Spot which was first seen in 1830. It is still visible, though its color, size and shape have changed over the years. Its greatest length has been 30,000 miles. The origin and nature of this feature are unknown.

The infrared spectrum of Jupiter reveals the presence of hydrogen, ammonia and methane. Perhaps some of the ammonia is in solid, crystalline form and contributes to the form of the bands. The low mean density suggests that the atmosphere is only a few hundred miles thick and that from there on down to the center it is a mixture of liquid hydrogen and other gases in solid and liquid form. It is doubtful that there is much of a rocky core. Most likely, the other three large planets are built on the same model. Other

Fig. 4-3. Jupiter photographed in blue light. Note the elongated red spot and the bands. The satellite Ganymede is the bright spot off the edge of Jupiter at the upper right and its shadow cast by the sun is near the top of the planet a little to the left. (Photographs from the Mount Wilson and Palomar Observatories.)

evidence for this structure comes from the planet's *oblateness* of $\frac{1}{15}$, the fraction by which the polar diameter differs from the equatorial one. Because of its short rotation period (9^h55^m) and large diameter, its equatorial rotation speed is very large; therefore the centrifugal force at the equator is large. The large oblateness is a result of the low rigidity of the planetary material. For rocky objects like the earth and Mars, the oblateness values are, respectively, $1/297$ and $1/192$.

Because of Jupiter's very large mass and gravitational attraction, it disturbs to an appreciable extent the orbits of all the other planets. The effect is even more pronounced on the orbits of comets because their masses are small.

Jupiter is known to be a radio source of considerable strength and interest. The subject is much too extensive to be treated here in any detail except to say that the radio intensity varies erratically and with the period.

4-15 Saturn

The telescopic appearance of the planet's surface is somewhat like that of Jupiter except that the bands are less distinct. The atmospheric composition is much the same except that the ammonia bands are weaker. Because the cloud surface temperature ($-215°F$) is lower than that of

Fig. 4-4.   Saturn and its ring system. (Photograph from the Mount Wilson and Palomar Observatories.)

Jupiter, one can assume that more of the ammonia is frozen out of the atmosphere. The planet's mean density is only 0.7 times that of water.

The planet's most distinct feature is its three rings. The outermost ring has a diameter of 171,000 miles and the innermost, very faint ring, has an inner diameter of 88,000 miles, leaving a space of only 7,000 miles to the planet's cloud surface. The rings seem to be only about 10 miles thick and they lie in the planet's equatorial plane.

What are the nature and origin of this unique ring system? They cannot be opaque solids because at times it is possible to see a bright star through a ring as the ring passes between us and the star. When the slit of a spectroscope is placed across the diameter of the rings, the Doppler shifts show that the inner edge of a ring has a greater orbital velocity than the outer edge, and by an amount that agrees with Kepler's Third Law. Therefore, the ring does not rotate as a solid sheet; if it did, the outer edge would have the greater orbital velocity. This information makes it seem probable that the rings are made up of a multitude of small, solid particles, each of which acts tiny satellite of the planet. It has been proposed that the ring materials rstals of solid ammonia, rock particles coated with ammonia and just k fragments.

s been suggested that the ring particles are fragments that were d by the tidally disruptive action of Saturn on a satellite which came se to the planet. For every planet there is a limiting distance, called e's limit, inside of which a satellite would be torn to pieces by the tidal forces of the planet but outside of which it would be safe. All of Saturn's satellites are outside the Roche limit for the planet, but the rings are inside. All other planetary satellites are outside the Roche limit appropriate to the planet. It is not known whether this theory is a true explanation of the formation of the rings, but it is an interesting possibility.

4-16 The Satellite Systems of Jupiter and Saturn

The satellite systems of each planet are remarkable subsolar systems in themselves. Jupiter has twelve satellites ranging from 113,000 miles to nearly 15 million miles from the planet's center. Their periods range from about one-half day to a little more than two years. The four brightest satellites, which were discovered by Galileo, have diameters of 1,800 to 3,100 miles; the faintest and smallest may have diameters as small as 20 miles. Note that the largest satellite is a little larger than Mercury. The nine satellites of Saturn have diameters of 2,850 miles to about 200 miles, distances of 100,000 miles to 8 million miles and periods from nearly a day to 550 days.

Jupiter's four most distant satellites and one of Saturn's revolve about their respective planets in the retrograde direction. It is thought that they (and perhaps some of the small direct motion satellites) are captured asteroids. Titan, the largest of Saturn's group, has a methane atmosphere—it is the only satellite in the solar system known to have an atmosphere. The four largest satellites of Jupiter have periods of from 1.77 days to 16.7 days. As seen from the earth these satellites are eclipsed periodically by the planet itself or they may pass into the planet's shadow and disappear for a time. These eclipses are easy to observe with even a small telescope.

4-17 Uranus and Neptune

Most of the information on these two planets is given in Table 4-1. Uranus has five satellites and Neptune two. At their great distances little surface detail can be seen. Both planets have cloud surface temperatures below −300°F, and it is probable that both planets are built on the Jupiter model. Uranus is unique in that its rotation axis lies nearly in the plane of its orbit.

4-18 The Discoveries of Uranus, Neptune and Pluto

Uranus was discovered in 1781 by William Herschel in England during an examination of the stars in the constellation Gemini. His first surmise th the object was a comet was proved wrong as soon as its orbit had ' computed. Uranus was the first planet discovered in modern times.

After some years it was observed that the motion of the plan agree with the motion predicted from its computed orbit. Since i of adjustment of the orbital elements would remove the discrepa suggestion was made that the motion of Uranus was being distu another, unknown planet. By a theoretical analysis based on the gravity and using these discrepancies, the position of the unknown planet was predicted. In 1846 the new planet, Neptune, was found close to the predicted position. The discovery was a great triumph for the law of gravity because the planet was discovered as a result of the gravitational effects of one body on another, and not by chance as in the case of Uranus.

In 1930 the ninth planet, Pluto, was discovered in a similar way by its disturbance (though much smaller) of the motions of Uranus and Neptune. A large region along the ecliptic in the sky was covered by pairs of photographic plates taken a week apart, and the pairs were examined for a moving object with the characteristic motion of a planet beyond Neptune. In February, 1930, the new planet was found nearly in the predicted position. It was given the name Pluto for the god of outer darkness. Its characteristics are given in Table 4-1. The full stories of the discoveries of Uranus, Neptune and Pluto are much too long to be discussed here, but they are recommended reading as chapters in the history of discovery.

Is there another planet beyond Pluto? Probably, but it can easily be shown that its disturbances of Neptune and Pluto would be slight and difficult to observe except over a long time interval. Only the photographic comparison method could be used in such a systematic, long-term survey, which would require much fainter limits of brightness than for Pluto. The number of star images that would have to be examined, the huge amount of time and the immense labor would hardly be worth even a positive result.

4-19 The Determination of the Mass of a Planet and a Satellite

The mass of an object can be determined only by the gravitational disturbance it produces in the motion of some other body. The mass of a planet can be determined if there is a body (a satellite) which the planet causes to move in orbital motion around itself. To do this we use Kepler's Third Law in the form $a^3/P^2 = m_p + m_s$; as before, a and P are given, respectively, in astronomical units and years, and the sum of the masses in terms of the solar mass. Therefore, knowing the semimajor axis of the satellite's orbit around the planet in astronomical units and the period of revolution in years, we obtain the sum of the masses of planet and satellite in terms of the solar mass. The masses of most of the satellites are so small compared to that of the planet that they may be neglected, with the result that the formula gives the planet's mass to a high degree of precision. For a planet such as Mercury or Venus, which is without a satellite, one can only measure the amount by which that planet disturbs the motion of another planet of known mass, such as the earth. The disturbances that Pluto (no satellite) causes in the motions of Uranus and Neptune are small, and its mass is not well determined.

As a rule the determination of the mass of a satellite is not easy. Our moon produces a disturbance in the earth's motion, but this effect is unusual and is not measurable for the other planets. In the case of Jupiter, one can get a good idea of the masses of the larger satellites by the way they disturb each other's motion. The mass of a small satellite can be estimated roughly by measuring its brightness and calculating how big it would be at its distance from the sun and the earth to be as bright as it is, assuming a reasonable value of the satellite's surface reflectivity. This estimated volume, coupled with what may be regarded as a reasonable density value of around three times that of water, gives some idea of its mass.

COMETS AND METEORS

4-20   Comets

Hardly an adult or teenager has not heard of—or in rarer cases seen— Halley's comet, which was so brilliantly beautiful in 1910 and which is so often portrayed with its long tail. The pictures are accurate, but the emphasis on this atypical comet has given a wrong impression of comets as a whole. Most comets are very faint objects that do not reach naked-eye visibility, and their photographs are not spectacular. Hundreds of comets have been observed since 1900 but only about two dozen have reached naked-eye brightness. At any one time a half-dozen faint comets may be under observation.

4-21   The Orbits of Comets

The average orbital eccentricity of comets' orbits is much higher than that for the planets, but individual values can range from zero to unity. The shortest known period is 3.3 years and the longest may be millions of years.

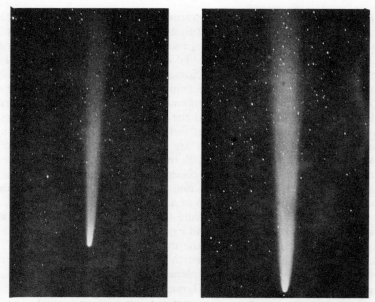

Fig. 4-5. **Two photographs of Halley's comet taken on May 12 (left) and May 15, 1910. In the left photograph the tail is 30 degrees long; in the right one, it is 40 degrees. (Photograph from the Mount Wilson and Palomar Observatories.)**

The orbital motion may be either direct or retrograde and the inclinations can have values from zero to ninety degrees.

However, there is a pronounced and significant difference between short and long period comets if one draws the line at about 150 years. In the former group, the average inclination and eccentricity are much smaller than in the long period group. Most of the short period comets have direct orbital motion just like the planets and an average aphelion distance near the orbit of Jupiter. Among the long period comets, the average inclination is high, the eccentricity is very large and the orbital motions are about evenly divided between direct and retrograde.

An appreciable number of comets have orbital eccentricities slightly greater than unity, i.e., hyperbolic orbits. Does this mean that these objects make only one pass at the sun? It can be shown that all of these comets moved in highly eccentric orbits before they entered the planetary region, but that close encounters with Jupiter or Saturn altered the orbits from ellipses to hyperbolas. Such comets will not be seen again. However, the reverse may take place: a close encounter with Jupiter may cause the period, eccentricity and inclination to become less, so that in time the comet acquires the characteristics of a short period comet. A gravitational encounter with Jupiter may even cause the retrograde motion of a comet to become direct.

4-22 The Changes in the Appearance of a Comet

As a comet approaches the sun from a great distance it is first seen as a faint, fuzzy, non-stellar patch. This *head* grows in size and brightness, and finally it develops a short *tail*. The tail points approximately away from the sun, and reaches its greatest length and brilliance when the comet is closest to the sun. After passing perihelion, the reverse process takes place until finally the comet fades away into invisibility. Since the tail always points away from the sun, as the comet travels away from the sun, the tail will precede the comet. When the object is fairly close to the sun, the head can often be resolved into a small star-like *nucleus* surrounded by a halo called the *coma*.

4-23 The Physical Nature of a Comet

When a comet is very far from the sun its spectrum is much like that of the sun's spectrum reflected from dust particles or from a solid mass. Close to the sun its spectrum is a composite of the reflected solar spectrum and the emission spectra of such molecules as C_2, OH, CN, CO, NH, CH and N_2. These gases are under very low pressure. Very probably these molecules are fragments of the molecules of water (H_2O), cyanogen (C_2N_2), carbon dioxide (CO_2), methane (CH_4) and ammonia (NH_3). The fragmentation is probably caused by the powerful action of the sun's ultraviolet radiation, which also excites the fragments and causes them to glow. The evidence is now very strong that the nucleus of a comet is a chunk of the frozen gases listed above. The ice mass does not sublime to gas when far from the sun where the temperature is low, but as it approaches the sun the heat causes sublimation to form the coma. Close in to the sun, the pressure of the sun's radiation and the solar wind ejects the gases from the coma to form the tail. The *solar wind* is the continuous breeze of charged particles, mainly protons from hydrogen, ejected from the sun. This pressure causes the tail to point away from the sun. Since the material of the tail is forever lost to the comet, its mass decreases and eventually the comet will cease to exist.

Very little can be said about the masses of comets except that they are very small. The mass of a comet can be determined only if it produces an appreciable disturbance in the motion of a body of known mass. Such a disturbance has never been observed. On one occasion, a comet passed right through the moon system of Jupiter but produced no measurable disturbance in the motion of any of the moons. All that one can do is to calculate what the mass of the nucleus would have to be in order not to effect a disturbance. From such information, and the density of ice, one can conclude that the nuclear diameter of a comet even as large as Halley's must be less than ½ mile. No comet nucleus has ever shown a disc to an observer using a telescope.

4-24   Meteors, Meteroids, and Meteorites

A *meteor* is the phenomenon produced in the earth's atmosphere when a *meteoroid* mass from outer space strikes and plunges into the atmosphere. It is commonly called a shooting star or falling star. If the meteoroid survives this catastrophic experience and reaches the earth's surface as a recognizable mass, it is called a *meteorite*. A meteor may appear as a very faint streak of light, or it may have the brilliance of a long fireball trail and be visible for hundreds of miles. Hundreds of millions of meteoroids strike the earth's atmosphere each day. They range in size from the tiny micrometeoroids weighing but a minute fraction of an ounce to the very rare ones weighing many tons.

4-25   The Meteoroid Impact With The Earth's Atmosphere

The impact velocity of a meteoroid with our atmosphere may be almost zero or as great as 44 mi/sec, depending on the relative orbital speeds and directions of motion of the two bodies. Most meteors are first seen at an altitude of about 80 miles and fade out at about 25 miles. Because of their tremendous speeds their kinetic energy per ounce may be enormous. Most of this energy is dissipated within a brief interval ranging from a fraction of a second to two or three seconds. The energy dissipates by pushing aside the air, exciting and ionizing the molecules and atoms, and heating the surface of the meteoroid. A glowing column of air and ablated material is left behind.

4-26   Meteor Swarms

About the middle of November each year, the number of meteors shows a perceptible increase and then a decrease lasting a few days. Most of the meteors radiate from a *radiant* in the constellation Leo and are called Leonids. This divergence from a radiant is a phenomenon of perspective and is the result of the meteoroids' traveling in parallel paths in space as they strike the earth's atmosphere. During the year it is possible to observe many swarms, each with its own radiant, although the hourly rate is very small for most of them. Let us note here that no swarm meteoroid has ever been known to become a meteorite.

By photographic triangulation using two telescopes placed some distance apart, one can determine the motion of the meteoroid before it struck our atmosphere. From these results one can determine that all the meteoroids from the same stream follow fairly closely the same orbit around the sun. Each radiant indicates a separate swarm moving in its own distinctive orbit. Clearly, we do not become aware of a swarm unless its orbit intersects the earth's orbit at some time during the year. Since the individual meteoroids may have orbital periods of some years, and, since we see some each year when the earth reaches the intersection, it appears that the meteoroids are strung out in a long chain all around the orbit. On some occasions, meteors from a given swarm are observed for several nights. This means that the earth takes that long to move across the swarm diameter, which may be several millions of miles.

4-27   The Structure and Composition of Swarm Meteoroids

Not uncommonly it is observed that a swarm meteoroid breaks up along the meteor path and the meteor fluctuates rapidly in brightness. From this and other evidence, it appears that many swarm meteoroids are not solid lumps like grains of sand, but are more like cotton fluff. They may be made up of a mass of crystalline material. Occasionally it is possible to obtain the spectrum of a bright meteor and to observe the emission lines of such elements as iron, magnesium, calcium and manganese. For some of the very fast meteoroids, the energy is so high that one can observe some of these metals in the ionized state.

4-28   The Relation Between Swarm Meteoroids and Comets

The principal evidence for such a relationship lies in the numerous cases of close correspondence between a comet's orbit and a specific swarm orbit. The theory that is involved here is often called the "Dirty Ice Theory."

According to this theory, the nucleus of a comet is made up of a chunk of ice of the several gases detected in the spectrum of a comet, and that imbedded in the ice are the meteoroid particles. As the comet approaches the sun and becomes warmer, the ice sublimes to form the coma and tail, and the solid particles are exposed at the surface of the nucleus. Since the gravitational attraction of the nuclear mass is very small, only a feeble force is required to eject the meteoroid. Rotation of the nucleus and small explosions or puffs of the subliming ice would be sufficient. The particles would be ejected in all directions. Those ejected forward or backward from the direction of motion of the nucleus string out along the comet's orbit and form the chain. Those ejected sidewise broaden the chain but continue in practically the same orbit. It must be noted that the speed of ejection of the particles will always be much smaller than the speed of the nucleus. Therefore, the orbit of the meteoroids will be practically the same as that of the comet from whose nucleus they originated. In time, planetary perturbations and solar radiation forces may alter this correspondence a great deal, and one can expect that eventually the orbits of the meteoroids will no longer resemble that of the comet.

Since the gases are lost to the nucleus, there must come a time when the ice is gone and the only evidence that there ever was a comet is the meteoroid swarm. There have been a number of cases in which a faint comet was discovered, observed for a few returns and seen no more. Somewhere in the solar system there must be a supply of comet nuclei.

4-29   Meteorites

Only very rarely is a meteoroid massive enough to survive the plunge through the atmosphere and reach the earth's surface as a meteorite. Meteorites range in mass from a fraction of an ounce to many tons, and they supply the astronomer with his only bird-in-hand sample of the universe beyond the earth.

The meteor phenomenon observed when such a massive body plunges to earth can be of extraordinary brilliance, and at night it may light up the landscape for many miles. Sometimes meteors are bright enough to be seen in daylight. At times they can be heard because of the shock wave produced by their rapid motion through the air. The sound may be a rumble like thunder or the sound of a distant train crossing a railroad trestle. Once in a while a massive meteoroid will fragment under the stress of impact and produce a shower of many pieces. On rare occasions the impact with the ground will produce a large crater.

In a rough sort of way, meteorites may be classified as either the *nickel-iron* or the *stoney* variety. The nickel-irons consist mainly of iron, with some nickel and relatively small amounts of other elements. The stoney type consists mainly of silicates some of which are similar to those found in terrestrial rocks. There are all gradations between these two broad types. Some fifty minerals have been identified in meteorites, and about an equal number of chemical elements.

The problem of observational selection is well illustrated by the numbers of meteorites in the two classes as they are found in museums. The great majority of all meteorite finds are of the nickel-iron variety, but most of those which have been seen to fall, and then recovered, are of the stoney type. One of the reasons for this discrepancy is that the stoney type have a lower breaking strength, so that they may fragment in the atmosphere or on striking rocky ground. The density of the nickel-irons is so much greater than that of the stoney type that—although both types may look like ordinary rock—the "heft" of a nickel-iron will easily distinguish it from an ordinary dark rock. The breaking strength of the nickel-irons is so much greater that they tend to stay in one piece and are easier to find.

Meteorites can be dated by the uranium-lead method. The resultant values vary from one object to another, but average somewhere between 4 and 5 billion years. It must be understood that this value represents the age of the meteorite in its present solid form. What transformations it went through before are not known. This age is fairly close to the value usually given for the age of the earth, and suggests that the earth and the meteorites were formed at about the same time.

Fig. 4-6. The Barringer meteor crater near Winslow, Arizona. (Photograph from the Yerkes Observatory.)

4-30 Meteorite Craters

From all over the world there is evidence of craters produced by meteorite impact. They range in diameter from a few feet to a few miles. There is a report of what may well be a fossil crater in South Africa which has a diameter of 40 miles. It could have been produced by a small asteroid. Almost all meteorite craters are nearly circular in outline. The shape of the crater seems to have little to do with the angle of impact. The shock wave of highly compressed air on the forward side of the meteorite plays a major role in blasting out and creating a circular crater much larger than the impacting body. The craters are much like those produced by an aerial bomb. However, not all circular craters are meteoritic in origin; several geologic processes can produce the same effect. One kind of evidence is in the presence around the crater of meteorite fragments that were blasted out in the explosion. A good example of this is Arizona's Barringer Crater, which is

4,000 feet in diameter. The rock formations around the edge of this crater have been badly fractured and turned upward by the force of the underground explosion. One of the best indicators is the presence of the mineral *coesite,* which is formed from quartz under very high pressures. Its presence in a crater is now thought to be proof positive of the crater's meteoritic origin. Some of the large circular lakes in eastern Canada are now confirmed as meteorite craters, in part because of the presence of coesite.

4-31   The Origin of Meteorites

It was earlier remarked that no swarm meteoroids have ever been known to reach the earth's surface. Their masses are too small to survive to the surface. While many shower meteoroids have retrograde orbits, there is no known case of a meteorite with a retrograde orbit. Meteorite orbits usually have small inclinations and eccentricities, and therefore they have planetary characteristics. The present theory of the origin of meteorites is that they were formed either by the disintegration of a small planet or by the collision (on at least one occasion) of two asteroids. The latter event would produce a great shower of direct orbital motion fragments, some of which would have orbits with eccentricities that would move them inside the earth's orbit at times, and hence on occasion to collide with the earth.

4-32   Micrometeorites

A large pan exposed to the open air for a week or so will collect a certain amount of dust. A careful examination of this material will reveal a number of particles about 1/10,000 inch in diameter which are composed largely of iron, and such elements as silicon and magnesium. Many of the particles will be spherical. It is thought that these are *micrometeorites.* A micrometeoroid is so small that it would not burn up in the atmosphere, but would be slowed and settle gradually to the earth's surface. Some of the particles may be cooled droplets of molten material from the surface of a larger meteoroid. Space satellites equipped with suitable detection devices have given evidence that there are micrometeoroids beyond the earth's atmosphere.

4-33   The Meteoroid Hazard to Space Travel

Any space vehicle beyond the earth's atmosphere will be bombarded by many meteoroids of all sizes, but the hazard has been much exaggerated. The outer shell of the vehicle would stop all micrometeoroids. A collision with an object the size of a walnut would be damaging to an extent depending upon where it struck the vehicle. A collision with one weighing several pounds might prove fatal to the mission, no matter where it struck. However, the space density of meteoroids large enough to seriously affect the vehicle and its occupants is so low that no serious problem is presented. The hazard per mile to space travel of a seriously damaging collision with a meteoroid is so much less than the hazard per mile to the operation of an automobile that even a trip to and from the moon may be undertaken in comparative safety. One can expect fatal accidents in the long run, but they will be rare.

4-34   The 1908 Siberian Meteorite(?)

On June 30, 1908, an extremely brilliant daylight meteor was observed in the Tunguska River area in central Siberia. The atmospheric shock wave rattled windows as far as 300 miles from the impact point and in time was registered on microbarographs all around the earth. Small tremors were felt up to 100 miles from the impact area. In the middle 1920's a Soviet government expedition to the area found craters up to 150 feet across. As far as 20 miles from this area, trees were found to have fallen with their tops pointing away from the crater area. The odd thing is that no trace of meteoritic material has ever been found, even though it seems perfectly clear that most of the effects observed were caused by a body from outer space. There is now fair agreement that the object was not the usual large meteoroid, but the nucleus of a small comet. The heat produced on impact with the atmosphere and the earth's surface vaporized the ice of the nucleus and the small dust particles imbedded in the ice, so that nothing solid remained. It is doubtful whether the object was larger than 100 feet in diameter.

4-35   The Origin and Evolution of the Solar System

With this background of descriptive details about the structure and behavior of objects in the solar system, the question naturally arises as to its origin and the evolutionary changes that have taken place. In Chapter 6 the formation and evolution of stars will be discussed. Because a star is a single body it is relatively much simpler than the solar system in all its wealth of detail, and for this reason the origin and evolution of the solar system is a very much more difficult problem. In this section, a brief discussion of four hypotheses will be presented, but no attempt will be made to do this in strict historical order.

The Random Capture Hypothesis

It is assumed in this hypothesis that the sun was already in existence and that as it moved through space it captured the cold objects that we call the planets. It is presumed that these objects were already formed. This theory is quite wrong on two counts. In the first place, the process of random capture would produce planetary orbits whose arrangement was completely at random in space with both direct and retrograde orbital motion. This is not the observed state of affairs in our solar system. In the second place, it is not possible for the sun (or any other star) to capture such an object. Any object in space would have a motion of its own so that as it moved in toward the sun its velocity would be greater than the escape velocity at any distance from the sun with the result that it would pass around the sun and on back out into space to be seen no more.

The Encounter Hypothesis

Once again it is assumed that the sun already exists and that another star approaches the sun, comes within a few solar radii of the sun, passes around it and escapes back into space. During this brief encounter which would last only a few hours while the two stars were close together, great tides were raised on each star and a large amount of gases were torn loose from each body. As in the example of water tides on the earth caused by the moon (Sec. 2-9), the tidal material would be ejected into the space between the two stars and also on opposite sides. Because the line joining the two stars is turning during the encounter, the disrupted gases would be set into rotation and, as the two stars separated, each would be accompanied by two tongues of gas rotating about each star. The hypothesis goes on to propose that condensations began in such gas which eventually cooled and contracted to form the present planets. By this means, each star would be accompanied by its own solar system. On the surface, this seems to account for a group of planets of all which revolve about the sun in the same direction and in nearly the same plane.

There are at least two fatal objections to this hypothesis. The first is that it is difficult, if not impossible, to see how any of this gas could be flung out into space as far as Neptune or Pluto and be set into orbital motion about the sun. Almost everyone has seen an ice skater begin a spin with her arms held out wide away from her body and has observed that as she pulls her arms in close she spins more rapidly. The reverse would be true if the skater started with her arms in close and then extended them away from her body: the rate of spin would slow down. In the same way, a gaseous mass revolving about the sun (when in close) would be revolving so slowly after having been flung out to a great distance that it would not move in anything like a circular orbit, but would fall back toward the sun in a highly elliptical one. Another objection is that the gas torn loose from each star would be so hot and the gas pressure within so high that the gravitational attraction of each mass would not be able to overcome the gas pressure which the greater mass of the sun was able to do. It can be shown that each mass could not cool fast enough to reduce the gas pressure to the point where gravity could take over and the mass could contract. Instead, each globule would expand into space and be lost to the sun. One more objection is that the stars in space are so far apart as compared to their diameters that the chance of such an encounter would be exceedingly small. There are further objections to the hypothesis that make it even more unsatisfactory.

The Nebular Hypothesis

Here it is assumed that there was in the beginning a gaseous nebula, roughly spherical in shape, as large or larger than the present solar system and that it was slowly rotating. Keeping in mind the analogy of the skater, as the nebula contracted under its own gravitational contraction, its rotation rate would increase and slowly flatten toward the plane of rotation. It was suggested that as the speed of rotation of the outer edge of the nebula increased it would finally reach the escape velocity and a ring of gas would break off. As the contraction of the main mass continued and it sped even further, successive rings would break off leaving, in the end, a rapidly rotating sun surrounded by a group of concentric, gaseous rings. The hypothesis proposed that the material in each ring had combined with others to produce a mass, and that a planet was formed from each one. The satellite systems would have formed in a similar way.

The main difficulty with this idea is that it can be easily calculated that if it were true, the sun should be rotating in a period of a few hours instead of the actual time of about 27 days. The sun has too little rotational motion. It is also very doubtful that the rings would have broken off during the condensation of the nebula. More likely the gas would have frittered away from the edge of the nebula. And even if the rings had formed, it is hard to see how the gas in each ring could have condensed into only one body or into any body at all.

The Proto-Planet Hypothesis

After a discussion of three failures, it is pleasant to turn to our newest hypothesis which does give a reasonable degree of satisfaction although it is far from total. As in the nebular hypothesis, it assumes the existence of a slowly rotating mass of cool gas and dust considerably larger than the present system of the planets. The gas consisted mainly of hydrogen and a little helium plus smaller amounts of the other chemical elements. As we shall see in Chapter 6, many such gaseous nebulae are known to exist elsewhere in space.

This nebula collapsed very rapidly under its own gravitational pull until most of the material was condensed into our present sun with the remaining few percent of the original mass revolving chaotically around the sun in a flattened disc as large as the present limit of the planets. This gas and dust was in turbulent motion with the result that large changes in density would take place from point to point in the nebula. Occasionally a condensation would form with a density and mass so high that its own gravitational attraction would prevent it from breaking up again. These permanent condensations of gas and dust are called the *proto-planets*. Each of the proto-planets must have been fairly massive; otherwise they could not have held together.

As each of the proto-planets moved around the sun all in the same direction as the rotating disc of dust and gas, they increased their masses by sweeping up more material. Even though the sun must have been quite hot during this period, the proto-planets were probably cold because the space between the proto-planets and the sun was still filled by large amounts of the opaque dust and gas. As time went on, some of the interplanetary material was swept up by the proto-planets and the remainder escaped into space beyond the solar system. As the interplanetary space became more transparent, the proto-planet atmospheres were warmed by the sun's heat and the temperature increased. This warming effect would be the most intense nearest to the sun. For those proto-planets nearest to the sun where the temperature was highest, the atmospheres escaped almost entirely, leaving behind only a solid core composed of the non-volatile materials of the solar nebula. For the more distant planets, the heating effect was much less so that Jupiter, Saturn, Uranus and Neptune are still much like they were in the proto-planet stage. The present atmospheres of the inner planets were probably formed by chemical reactions in the solid material and ejected to form an atmosphere in the manner of volcanic eruptions.

When the proto-planets were quite large, they were most probably rotating in both clockwise and counterclockwise directions. In time the sun caused tidal motions and friction in each of the proto-planets so that after a while each body rotated (ccw) once per revolution about the sun, in the same direction as the sun was rotating, just as now the moon rotates once per month in its revolution about the earth. However, as each proto-planet contracted more, it would try to speed its rotation rate just as in the case of the skater. Eventually it would be rotating independently of the sun and in the counterclockwise direction.

The satellites were most probably formed as condensations in each proto-planet's own rotating nebula. However, our own moon is so large compared to the earth that it is thought to have been another smaller proto-planet captured by the earth. As we have seen before in this chapter, some of the retrograde satellites are probably asteroids captured in more recent times.

The asteroids in the belt between Mars and Jupiter are possibly the result of many proto-planets formed in that region. Because of the great gravitational pull of Jupiter, it seems reasonable that any object in that region as large as proto-Mars would be disrupted into smaller fragments. The known irregular shape of many asteroids (Sec. 4-12) argues for the breakup of a larger body by Jupiter or the collision between two large asteroids to form a large number of fragments.

The comets might well be small condensations formed in the original nebula when it was still very large and contracting. These cometary nuclei were left behind as the nebula continued to shrink. This suggests that there now exists a large reservoir of comets well beyond the distance of Pluto and in all directions from the sun. Some nuclei could have formed in the later stages of the contraction when the nebula had become a flattened disc. These might have had their orbits disturbed to such an extent by the massive outer planets that they were pulled out to great distances from the sun.

A serious objection to this hypothesis (similar to the objection to the nebular hypothesis) is that it would have left the sun rapidly rotating. It appears that gravitational forces alone cannot explain the slowly rotating sun, but theories now exist that involve the braking action on the sun by strong magnetic fields generated in the ionized gas of the solar nebula. The subject is much too broad to permit any more than mention here.

Very briefly, this is a condensed version of the proto-planet hypothesis. It has had a fair number of successes, but many facts about the origin and evolution of our solar system remain to be explained—a great deal of thoughtful work remains to be done. One interesting idea that emerges from this hypothesis is that if the hypothesis is true, even in a general way, then there ought to be solar systems accompanying many other stars. Quite possibly there are many solar systems in space with at least one planet that sustains intelligent life.

QUESTIONS

1. When Venus is in the crescent phase close to inferior conjunction, it is possible to see the narrow crescent continued all the way around as a faint ring of light. Suggest a reason for this phenomenon.
2. Would you expect Mars to show phases? Explain.
3. Draw a diagram to show the circumstances under which the gravitational disturbances of Jupiter could convert the orbit of a comet of long period and high eccentricity into a shorter period and less eccentric orbit with either direct or retrograde motion.
4. What effects would you expect to observe if the earth passed through the tail of a comet?
5. How would you expect the seasons on Mars to compare with those on the earth?
6. The diameter and mass of the sun are, respectively, 108 and 330,000 times those of the earth. Calculate the velocity of escape from the photosphere of the sun.
7. Attempts have been made to observe the impact of a meteoroid on the moon by looking for the flash on the dark half of the moon at first and third quarters. No impact flash has ever been seen. Suggest reasons for this failure.
8. From the figures in Table 4-1, show that when Pluto is at perihelion it is closer to the sun than is Neptune. What do you think is the probability of a collision between Pluto and Neptune?

Chapter 5

The Sun. An Introduction to the Stars

Our sun is the nearest star, and it is the only one which is seen as a disc instead of an unresolved point of light. It is possible to examine the sun's disc in great detail—this can be done for no other star. The sun is almost the sole source of radiant energy in the solar system, and of course life on earth would be impossible without it. The light from the stars is negligible compared to that from the sun. The presence of fossils in pre-Cambrian rocks is evidence that the sun's surface temperature and the energy we receive from it have changed but little in the last billion or so years.

5-1   The Physical Structure of the Sun

The mass of the sun is 2.2×10^{27} tons, 330,000 times more massive than the earth. The sun contains 99.8% of the mass of the solar system. Its diameter is 864,000 miles and its average distance from the earth is not quite 93 million miles (one a.u.). The mean density of the solar material is 1.4 times that of water. Because the sun is so hot throughout all its volume, all of its matter must be in the gaseous state.

The visible surface of the sun is called the *photosphere* (Greek for "light sphere"). Above it the gases are almost entirely transparent and below it they are opaque. Just above the photosphere is a layer called the *chromosphere* (Greek for "color sphere") because of its reddish color, which can be seen when the photosphere is hidden during a total solar eclipse. The lower level of the chromosphere is called the *reversing layer* because it is the main source of the absorption lines in the solar spectrum. In the chromosphere and extending through it well up into the corona are the *prominences,* red in color, which can be seen at the sun's edge (the limb) during a total solar eclipse. At the same time one can observe the *corona,* a faint, white solar halo, which has been observed at times to be several solar radii above the photosphere. None of these layers is sharply bounded, but instead they merge into one another. The average temperature of the photosphere is 5,750° K. At this temperature the maximum of the spectral energy distribution is in the visible region and here is found a large fraction of the total solar radiation.

Theoretical studies have shown that the sun's interior temperature rises rapidly below the photosphere and probably reaches 15 million°K at the center. Not far below the photosphere the temperature is so high that most of the atoms are completely ionized. As we will discuss in the next chapter, it now seems obvious that the sun's energy source is the nuclear transformation of hydrogen into helium. Since the mass of the sun is great and the nuclear process is a very efficient one, it appears that the sun is capable of shining with its present brilliance for many billions of years.

5-2   The Surface Phenomena of the Sun

Early visual observations and the long record of later photographic data have revealed an incredible amount of detail. It is regretable that such diverse information can be obtained for no other star.

Telescopes carried by balloon to 80,000 feet, and well above most of the disturbances of the earth's atmosphere, reveal in beautiful detail the photospheric *granules* with diameters of from 300 to about 1,000 miles. They have a honeycomb appearance of bright spots surrounded by darker boundaries. A particular granule has a lifetime of only a few minutes. From Doppler shift observations it is clear that the bright, central region of a granule is a hot rising column of gas which cools by radiation, the darker gas then sinking back down around the edge of the granule to become heated again and rise once more. These granules are an important mechanism for the transport of heat from the solar interior.

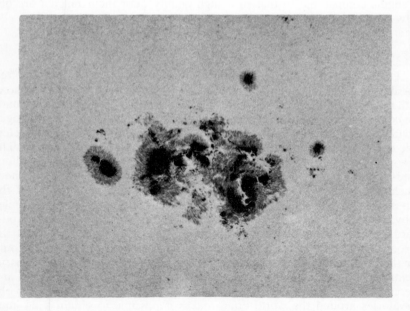

Fig. 5-1.   A large, complex sun spot group. (Photograph from the Mount Wilson and Palomar Observatories.)

The most obvious features are the *sun spots*. The smallest spots are about 1,000 miles across and the largest have reached diameters of 100,000 miles, but the latter are rare. The larger ones can be seen by the naked eye through fog, smoke or a dark absorbing glass. Sunspots are roughly circular structures consisting of two well defined parts. The central, darker region is the *umbra* and the outer, brighter ring is the *penumbra*. The umbra is about 1,500 degrees cooler than the photosphere outside the penumbra. Because of its much lower temperature the umbra radiates a smaller luminous flux than the photosphere and is darker by contrast. If the umbra could be seen by itself it would be intensely bright.

Most spots occur in pairs or in groups dominated by two large spots. The line joining the centers of a pair is about parallel to the sun's equator. From observations of spots it is known that the sun does not rotate as a solid. The rotation period at the equator is 25 days and increases to 27½ days at latitude 30 degrees. Since spots are rarely seen beyond this latitude, the rotation period is found from Doppler shift observations of opposite limbs of the sun. The period increases to 35 days at latitude 75 degrees. Almost all spots are found between latitudes 5 and 35 degrees in each hemisphere. They are scarce in the narrow equatorial region and the polar zones.

The lifetimes of spots range from as short as a day to a few months for those that grow to large size. A spot is first observed as a dark dot about 1,000 miles across on the photosphere. Most spots fade away in a day or two but those that persist may grow into groups 200,000 miles across. One of the most interesting aspects of sun spots is their magnetic polarity. Field strengths comparable to that of a high quality permanent magnet are observed.

5-3 . Prominences

Under the conditions of a natural or artificial total eclipse it is often possible to see large, bright streamers or clouds above the photosphere, with their base in the chromosphere and near the limb of the sun. The clouds are composed largely of hydrogen, but contain some calcium. The hydrogen clouds are red because so much of the emission is at one of the characteristic emission lines of hydrogen, at the wavelength 6,563 Å in the red. The *quiescent* type of prominence may cover the sun's surface for tens of thousands of miles and be equally as high. Sometimes it persists for days without much change in appearance. The *eruptive* variety may be "blown" off the sun as fast as 400 miles per second and finally disappear a million miles above the photosphere. The *fountain* prominences show inward and/or outward motions from a spot group. At one time the prominences and the corona could be studied only at the time of a total eclipse of the sun and only for the few minutes of the eclipse duration. Astronomers now have instruments for the production of artificial eclipses, so that the prominences and the corona can be studied on any clear day. A network of these solar observatories around the world often makes it possible to obtain a 24-hour record of the sun's behavior. The reason for prominences is not clearly known. For some years, solar astronomers have been working on the prob-

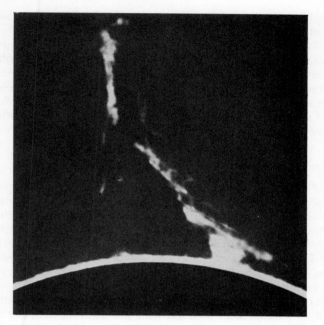

Fig. 5-2.   A solar prominence 570,000 miles high photographed in the violet light of the calcium K line. (Photograph from the Mount Wilson and Palomar Observatories.)

lem of the correlation and interdependence of all solar phenomena. One of their most fascinating exhibitions is a time lapse motion picture of a prominence, covering the motion of a prominence for a period of an hour or more with a projection time of only a few minutes.

5-4   Some Solar Instruments

For a long time there have been solar telescopes of the tower type. This type uses a long focus lens to produce a large image of the sun so that the disc can be examined in detail. To avoid "seeing" disturbances so prevalent during the day, the lens is mounted on top of a tower and the image is formed near the ground where it can be photographed or the light can be examined with a large, high dispersion spectrograph. The 60-foot and 150-foot towers at the Mount Wilson Observatory are examples.

Since World War II the *coronagraph* has come into general use in solar observatories. In this instrument the image of the sun falls on a blackened disc or cone just large enough to block the disc of the sun. The light from the corona and the prominences continues past the disc until finally it is imaged for photography by a camera lens. Since the light of the corona and the prominences is so faint compared to that from the solar disc, great care must be taken to reduce scattered light in the instrument and to mount the telescope at high altitudes where there is much less light scattering dust in the atmosphere. With this instrument an artificial eclipse of the sun can be produced at will on any clear day.

One of the older but still useful instruments, the *spectroheliograph,* will not be described here except to remark that it is capable of obtaining a photograph of the whole sun in just one narrow wavelength range. When it is set for the red line of hydrogen at 6,563 Å, it will obtain a photograph of the sun showing only the distribution of glowing hydrogen. By this means, when used at other wavelength settings it can reveal the distribution of any other element, such as calcium.

5-5   Solar Flares

One of the most spectacular and short lived of all solar phenomena is the *solar flare*. Flares appear as very bright spots in the photosphere and usually near a spot group. A typical flare reaches maximum brightness in a few minutes and then fades away more slowly, disappearing in about a half hour. Flare temperatures are much higher than those of the photosphere and they emit large amounts of ultraviolet light. The reason for flares is not known and it is not possible to predict their occurrence. However, they are known to be more common when sun spots are more numerous.

The percentage change in brightness during a flare is very small, but if the same flare were to occur on a star with one-tenth the diameter and hence one-one hundredth the area of the sun, the change in brightness would be easily perceptible. In recent years discoveries have been made of a number of "flare stars," in which there may be a sudden increase in brightness (in a matter of minutes or seconds) and then a slow fading. These stars are normally red and are dwarfs with respect to the sun's size. During a flare, the color changes from red to blue and the star may become a hundred times brighter. It is probable that this phenomenon is a local flare much like the solar flares except that on these dwarf stars the flare has a surface area not much smaller than the star itself. There is some data to show that at these times there is also a radio noise flare, just as there is when a solar flare takes place.

5-6   The Solar Corona

The *corona* is a large white halo around the sun that extends above the photosphere for several million miles. Its total light is about one-millionth that of the photosphere. The *outer* corona exhibits a spectrum like that of the sun, indicating that it is made up of small, reflecting particles.

The *inner* corona is more interesting. Its spectrum consists of rather broad emission lines superimposed on a continuous spectrum with no absorption lines. For many years the wavelengths of these emission lines could not be identified with those of any known chemical elements, and for a time there was serious talk of a new element named "coronium." It was later discovered that these lines come from very highly ionized atoms of such elements as iron, calcium and nickel. Some of these atoms have lost as many as 15 electrons. One way to produce atoms which have lost so many electrons

Fig. 5-3. The solar corona photographed at the time of a total solar eclipse. Note the streamers near the magnetic poles of the sun. (Photograph from the Mount Wilson and Palomar Observatories.)

is for the coronal temperature to be so high that the thermal velocities of the atoms would cause intense collisional ionization. This would also account for the broad emission lines: their normal width would be greatly increased by Doppler broadening caused by the very large radial velocities of the emitting atoms in the coronal gas. If equipartition of energy existed between the relatively massive ionized atoms and the much less massive but relatively numerous electrons, the average electron velocity ought to be far higher. The scattering of the sun's photospheric light by these electrons would result in such a large Doppler broadening that the solar absorption lines would be completely smeared out and the scattered solar spectrum would look like a continuous spectrum. This type of reasoning now leads astronomers to believe that the temperature of the inner corona is about 1 million°K, far higher than that of the photosphere. It is not at all clear just how this elevated temperature is maintained.

5-7 The Sun Spot Cycle

It has been known since 1851 that the numbers of sun spots have a rough periodicity with an average of nearly 11 years. At spot minimum there may be several successive days when no spots are seen. The plot of sun spot numbers against time shows a relatively rapid rise to maximum from minimum in a time of 4 to 5 years and then a slower decline to the next minimum. At sun spot maximum it may be possible to see 100 spots at a time. The general rapid rise to maximum and slower decline to minimum is characteristic of all cycles, but the time between successive maxima varies from 9 to 14 years.

If we consider only spot pairs we find that the line joining their centers is about parallel to the sun's equator, and so we may speak of a "lead" and a "following" spot in a pair. In any one cycle the magnetic polarity (N or S) of the lead spot will be the same for all pairs in one hemisphere and just the reverse in the other. In the next cycle the polarity of the lead spots will reverse between hemispheres from what it was in the preceding cycle.

At the beginning of a new cycle at spot minimum, the new spots of that cycle will appear in small numbers around latitude 30 degrees in both hemispheres. As the cycle progresses and the number of spots increases, older ones die out and newer ones appear at progressively lower latitudes, with the result that during a cycle the average spot latitude decreases to about 5 degrees at the cycle's end. Toward the end of a cycle there is an overlap of about 2 or 3 years between cycles; during this time one can see spots of the old cycle around 5 degrees latitude and spots of the new cycle around 30 degrees latitude.

5-8   The Solar Spectrum

The spectrum of the solar disc is of the absorption line type. Because the sun is so bright it is easy to obtain its spectrum at very high dispersion, which reveals a great deal of detail. Thousands of absorption lines have been measured. When their wavelengths are compared with laboratory values about 60 chemical elements reveal themselves in the reversing layer. There may be some elements whose lines show only in the ultraviolet or infrared parts of the spectrum which are cut off by the earth's atmosphere. Rocket and satellite observations from above the atmosphere will probably settle this question. Most of the absorption lines result from neutral atoms, some are caused by atoms easily ionized at the sun's temperature and others are produced by molecules, particularly in the cool region of sun spots.

5-9   Radio Noise From The Sun

During World War II radar instruments showed that the sun emits radio noise. It is now known to do so over a wide range of wavelengths. The opacity of the solar atmosphere for radio waves increases with increasing wavelength. At values of 10 to 20 meters the apparent size of the sun is large because the energy comes from the extended corona. For wavelengths around a few centimeters (an inch or two) the corona is transparent and the sun appears smaller because these shorter waves come from just above the photosphere.

Around spot minimum the radio sun is "quiet." The radio brightness is about that to be expected from a body of the sun's photospheric temperature. At spot maximum the noise level is much higher and subject to very large fluctuations. At such times enormous bursts may occur with an intensity a million times that of the quiet sun.

5-10   The Effects of Solar Activity on the Earth

At the time of a solar flare considerable interference with radio communications is immediately observed. This is due to the great increase in ultraviolet light from the flare, which causes increased ionization in our ionosphere. This produces disturbances in the radio reflectivity of the ionospheric layers because radio waves are reflected by an ionized gas. When the flare subsides, the situation soon returns to normal. The appearance of the flare is also accompanied by disturbances in the earth's magnetic field.

In addition to the enhanced ultraviolet radiation from a flare there is also an increase in the intensity of the *solar wind,* which consists of a stream of electrons and protons from the sun. Because these particles travel at speeds only as high as 1,000 mi/sec instead of at the velocity of light the particles require a day or more to reach the earth. The intensified solar wind causes strong auroral displays when the particles collide with the earth's atmosphere and excite its atoms and molecules into emission. The arrival of the cloud of particles often causes worldwide disturbances in the earth's magnetic field that may persist for days.

For a long time attempts have been made to correlate sun spot activity and the earth's weather but no recognizable effects seem to be present. This may be in part because so many factors influence the weather. Solar radiation is certainly one of them, but there are many others and the situation is not simple. However, there does seem to be a pronounced correlation between the thickness of the annual tree rings in some areas and the time in the sun spot cycle.

AN INTRODUCTION TO THE STARS

Before we begin our study of stars as individuals or groups it is desirable to understand a number of concepts and techniques and to learn a certain nomenclature. Our sun is an average sort of star in many ways. There are stars as much as 100,000 times brighter or fainter than our sun. Some dwarf stars are only 1/100 the solar diameter and a very few are so large that they could include the whole of the earth's orbit. The range in mass seems to be from a little less than 1/100 the sun's mass to perhaps a little less than 100 times as great. Surface temperatures range from as low as 2,500°K to as high as 50,000°K.

5-11   Constellations

Modern astronomers have inherited from the dim past the custom of dividing up the whole sky into 88 areas called constellations. Most of the constellation names and forms have come to us from the Greeks, preserved for us through the Dark Ages by the Arabic civilization. Most of the names are Latin translations of the Greek names. These groupings are useful, just as it is useful to be able to refer to a general area of the United States such as the Pacific Northwest or the Gulf Coast Region. If you tell an astronomer that you are working in Cygnus he will know that this is a constellation about halfway between the north celestial pole and the equator in the northern hemisphere, that it is best seen in the summer sky and that it is also a Milky Way constellation.

Most of the star configurations in the constellations do not look like the objects after which they were named—they were never intended to do so, but were only named in honor of those objects. Some constellations such as Corona Borealis (the northern crown) and Lyra (the harp) do resemble the objects.

The naming of stars is such a complicated subject that reference will be made to only two systems. Many of the brighter stars have proper names such as Vega, Arcturus, Alferatz or Betelgeuse, and often they are Arabic names. Another system indicates the star's location by assigning it a Greek letter and following this by the genitive of the constellation name. The brightest star in a constellation is usually called alpha, the next beta and so on. As an example, Vega is the brightest star in the constellation Lyra. Its "Greek letter designation" would be *alpha Lyrae.*

The study of constellations and star names can be a rewarding past-time for the non-professional. Although a useful set of star charts appears in Appendix 2, if one is interested in charts of greater detail, he should purchase a good star atlas such as is listed in Appendix 1.

5-12   Stellar Distances. The Stellar Parallax

As seen in Sec. 1-11 the parallax of a star in seconds of arc is the reciprocal of its distance in parsecs. In general, except where it would be awkward to do otherwise, we will give distances in light years. One parsec is 3.26 light years. Stellar distances are of the greatest importance to the astronomer because they enable him to understand the important spatial arrangement of stars and to determine certain of their physical properties. The direct method for the determination of stellar parallax consists in obtaining over a period of a few years a series of photographs of the star and its comparison field. These photographs are taken about six months apart at opposite ends of that diameter of the earth's orbit which is perpendicular to the direction of the star. The change in position of the parallax star on the plate is measured with reference to a group of fainter comparison stars which are assumed to be more distant. By this technique the smallest reliable parallax that can be measured is about $0''.020$, which corresponds to a distance of 50 parsecs or about 160 light years.

5-13   Radial Velocity and Proper Motion

The motion of a star in our line of sight, known as its *radial velocity,* is obtained by measuring the wavelength shift of the lines in the star's spectrum on a photographic plate with respect to some comparison spectrum such as that of iron. Individual line shifts are each converted into line velocities and the average is taken. This value is then corrected for the motion of the earth in its orbit, giving the star's radial velocity with respect to the sun. See Sec. 3-15 on the Doppler effect.

A star's *proper motion* is its yearly change in direction, measured in seconds of arc, which results from the sun's space motion, the star's space motion and the direction and distance to the star. A little thought will show that on the average the proper motion of a star will increase with decreasing distance from the sun, and that a good statistical way to look for nearby stars is to find those with large proper motion.

5-14 The Stellar Magnitude System

Along with the *Almagest*, Ptolemy included a star chart and catalogue to which he assigned numbers for brightness, 1 for the brightest and 6 for the faintest. Much later it was shown that the light from the average first magnitude star was nearly 100 times greater than that from the average sixth magnitude star. It is now known that the eye's response to light is not linear, but logarithmic. About 1850, astronomers made the arbitrary decision that the difference of brightness of five magnitudes was to correspond *exactly* to a luminosity ratio of 100:1. As a result, for any magnitude difference Δm, the ratio of the luminosities is expressed as

$$l_1/l_2 = \left[\sqrt[5]{100} \right]^{\Delta m} = (2.512 + \ldots)^{\Delta m}$$

The fifth root of 100 is close to 2.512. If Δm (read: delta m) is unity the ratio is 2.512. If the magnitude difference is 2 the ratio of brightness is 2.512 $\times$ 2.512, or about 6.25, and so on for any magnitude difference. For Δm equal to 6 (5 + 1) the ratio is 100 $\times$ 2.512 or about 250. The magnitude number increases as the star becomes fainter. This may seem an odd way to express brightness differences, but it is convenient in that it compresses a ratio of brightness from what might be a very large number to a conveniently small one. As an example let us suppose that the brightness ratio for two stars is 100 million (100,000,000). This can be written as 100 $\times$ 100 $\times$ 100 $\times$ 100. Each one of the 100's corresponds to 5 magnitudes and there are four 100's. Hence this brightness ratio is the *sum* of four 5's, or 20 magnitudes—a much smaller number.

The star's magnitude depends on its temperature or color; hot stars are brighter in the blue than in the yellow-green (visual region) and red stars are the reverse. Thus one can speak of a star's ultraviolet, blue, visual or red magnitude. We shall confine our use of magnitudes to the visual ones.

5-15 Apparent and Absolute Magnitudes. The Distance Modulus

Apparent magnitudes are the measures of stellar brightness as we see them in the sky. Because of very great ranges in distances they are not usually a measure of the true brightness of one star relative to that of another. If a star could be brought closer to us, it would become brighter and its apparent magnitude (m) would become smaller in number. Since stars have a very wide range of intrinsic luminosities, it is useful to have a system whereby this value can be expressed in magnitudes. The astronomer defines the *absolute magnitude* (*M*) as the apparent magnitude that a star would have if it were brought from its present distance to a distance of ten parsecs (32.6 light years). Consider the following example (for convenience parsecs will be used). A star at 40 parsecs (130.4 light years) is four times farther away than at 10 parsecs. If brought to 10 parsecs it would be 4 times closer and, by the inverse square law of brightness changes, it would be 16 times brighter. (The inverse square law of brightness means that if the distance of a source of light is *increased* by 2, 3 or 4 times its present distance from the observer, the brightness of the source will *decrease,* respectively, by 4, 9, or 16 times. The reverse will be true if the source is brought closer to the observer.) This is very nearly the same as 2.512 × 2.512 × 2.512, which means that the star would be 3 magnitudes brighter. If the star had an *m* of +9 at 40 parsecs its apparent magnitude at 10 parsecs would become +6, and by definition its *M* would be +6. The difference *m* − *M* is 3. This number is called the *distance modulus,* which means that it is the number of magnitudes by which a star becomes brighter when it is brought from its present distance to ten parsecs. One can see that in effect the distance modulus is just another way of expressing the distance of a star.

Let us consider another example: Let the distance modulus of a star be 10, which means that the star is 10 magnitudes fainter at its present distance than at a distance of 10 parsecs. Ten magnitudes may be written as 5 + 5; since each five magnitudes corresponds to a ratio of brightness of 100 times, the 10-magnitude difference is equal to a brightness ratio of 100 × 100, or 10,000 times. But by the inverse square law a change of brightness of 10,000 times is the result of a distance change of 100 times, or the square root of 10,000. Therefore, the star is 100 times farther away than 10 parsecs, or its distance is 1,000 parsecs (3,260 light years). We shall use the idea of distance modulus a number of times in later discussions.

5-16   Stellar Spectra and the Spectral Sequence

Up to the present the spectra of about a half-million stars have been photographed. Almost all stellar spectra are of the absorption type, although a few have emission lines. After a great deal of early study it was found that almost all stellar spectra could be placed in a sequence called the *spectral sequence,* of which there are seven main classes designated O, B, A, F, G, K and M. Except for class types O and M there are ten subdivisions in each class. With the exception of type O, representative samples are given in Fig. 5-4. One of the greatest discoveries in astronomy was the revelation that the spectral sequence is really a *temperature sequence.* The type O stars are the hottest and those of type M are the coolest. A brief description of each type follows.

Type O. Surface temperature 50,000°K. The few lines are due to ionized silicon, helium, oxygen and nitrogen. H (hydrogen) lines very weak. Color blue.

Type B. Temperature 16,000°K. Neutral helium, but none ionized. Singly ionized oxygen and silicon. H lines stronger. Color blue-white.

Type A. Temperature 9,000°K. Strong, broad H lines. Singly ionized magnesium and faint lines of neutral metals begin to appear. Color white.

Type F. Temperature 7,000°K. H lines weaker than in type A but still strong. Numerous lines of neutral metals chromium, iron and calcium, but singly ionized metals still show faintly. Color yellow-white.

Type G. Temperature 5,500°K. H lines continue to weaken. Most lines are of neutral atoms. Singly ionized calcium strong, but neutral calcium weak. Color yellow. Sun is type G2.

Type K. Temperature 4,500°K. Most lines from neutral metals. H lines very faint. Singly ionized calcium strongest, but neutral calcium stronger than in type G. Absorption bands of molecules begin to appear. Color orange to red.

Type M. Temperature 3,000°K. Practically all lines from neutral metals. H lines barely visible. Strong molecular bands of titanium oxide. Color red.

5-17 *The Interpretation of the Spectral Sequence*

In a general way most stars can be regarded as being constructed much like the sun, with a photosphere emitting continuous radiation and above it a reversing layer whose elements absorb at their characteristic wavelengths to produce an absorption spectrum. The strength of the absorption lines of an element will depend to a large extent on the number of atoms in an absorbing column through the reversing layer. At low temperatures the thermal velocities will be small and almost all the atoms will be in the neutral state. As the temperature rises the number of singly ionized atoms will increase at the expense of the neutral ones. At even higher temperatures there may be almost no neutral atoms. Most will be singly ionized and some will be doubly ionized, and so on toward higher temperatures. Therefore, at any particular temperature the appearance of the spectrum will be directly related to the atoms present in the neutral or ionized state. It is important to realize here that if in the reversing layer there should be equal numbers of atoms of two separate chemical elements, they need not produce the same amount of absorption. Some atoms are better absorbers than others. Again it must be realized that some atoms are harder to ionize than others. As an example, helium is hard to ionize and hence it appears in that state in only the hottest stars. On the other hand, calcium is rather easy to ionize and its lines are the strongest in the much cooler stars.

The H lines in Fig. 5-4 are in the wavelength range from 3,900 Å to 4,900 Å. Those that appear in this range arise from transitions from the second energy level in that atom to higher levels (Sec. 3-17). At low temperatures most of the H atoms are in the ground state, and only a few are available for transition from the second to higher states. Hence the H lines in the above range are weak. As the temperature rises, the population of the second level increases, more H atoms are in a condition to absorb from the second level to higher levels and, hence, the lines strengthen. At much higher temperatures many of the H atoms become ionized and, therefore, fewer are available to absorb. As a result the lines become weak again.

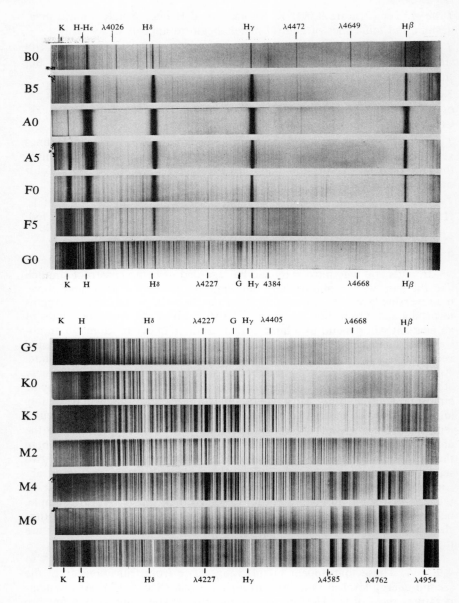

Fig. 5-4. Some representative examples in the spectral sequence. The letters
K and H refer to the lines of singly ionized calcium. The letter H followed by
Greek letters marks hydrogen lines. λ4227 is a line of neutral calcium, and
λ4668 is due to helium. (Photo from University of Michigan Observatory.)

In Fig. 5-4 observe the K line of singly ionized calcium (CaII) and the line 4,227 Å of neutral calcium (CaI). The neutral line is strong in the cool stars, but weakens as the temperature increases and more ionization takes place. Then the line of CaII strengthens, reaches a maximum strength and then weakens again in the very hottest stars, as the number of singly ionized atoms is decreased to produce the doubly ionized type for which no absorption lines occur in the wavelength range shown.

5-18 The Hertzsprung-Russell Diagram

Shortly after 1910 the American astronomer Henry Norris Russell and the Danish astronomer Ejnar Hertzsprung discovered a powerful correlation between spectral type and absolute magnitude. When the absolute magnitude (M) and the spectral types of many stars are plotted together as seen in Fig. 5-5, two main features are observed. The great majority of stars for which data are available lie in a narrow band called the *main sequence,*

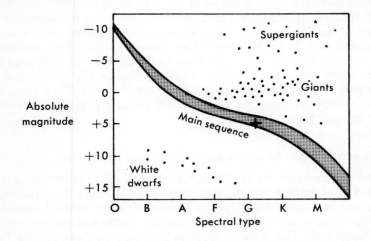

Fig. 5-5. The Hertzsprung-Russel diagram.

which runs across the diagram from about $M = -10$ for the hottest type O stars to about $M = +15$ for the coolest type M stars. Most of the other stars, from types G through M, are in another broad band above the main sequence in a region of the giants and supergiants. The position of the sun is marked with a cross on the main sequence. From one end of the main sequence to the other there is an extreme magnitude difference of 25 magnitudes, corresponding to a luminosity ratio of 10 billion to one. Note that at a type such as K there is a difference of several magnitudes between a giant and a main sequence star of the same type. Since the energy flux per unit area and unit time depends on the fourth power of the absolute temperature (which is the same for both stars), the K giant must have a much larger surface area and diameter than the main sequence K star. The quoted luminosity ratio of 10 billion to one between the hottest O star and the coolest M type does not represent the ratio of surface areas, because the O star is much hotter and puts out a great deal more light per unit area and time than does the main sequence M.

Well below the main sequence is another less conspicuous sequence called the *white dwarfs*. The adjective "white" comes from the fact that the first of these to be discovered, the faint companion of the bright star Sirius (alpha Canis Majoris), is white. The adjective is still used even though some white dwarfs are yellow. A particular white dwarf, say of type F, will be several magnitudes below the main sequence. Since an F star on the main sequence and the type F white dwarf have the same surface temperature, the white dwarfs must be much smaller. Many are about the size of the earth. However, their mass is about equal to that of our sun, and from this we conclude that the density of the white dwarf material must be exceedingly high. Densities of up to 100,000 times that of water are not uncommon. A cubic inch of such material would weigh not quite two tons! This unusual state of matter may be partly explained by saying that most of the atoms are stripped bare of their electrons right down to the nucleus, thus allowing the gas to be highly compressed. It appears that white dwarfs are dying stars and that they are the last stage in the evolution of a star. They have lost almost all of their hydrogen and other nuclear fuels, so that they shine only by their internal heat.

5-19 Spectroscopic Absolute Magnitudes and Distances

Within certain limits the H-R diagram can be used to determine stellar distances. Let us assume that the star of unknown distance is on the main sequence and that its spectral type is known. Reading upward from the spectral type scale to the main sequence and then to the left, one obtains its absolute magnitude. The distance modulus and then the distance (see Sec. 5-15) follows from the absolute magnitude M and its measured apparent magnitude m. The method is somewhat complicated by the fact that the main sequence has a real vertical spread in M at any spectral type. It can only be stated here that the vertical position of the star on the main sequence can be determined from an examination of spectral lines, which are sensitive to luminosity but not temperature, and hence to obtain a more accurate value of M. Furthermore, an examination of the lines will show whether the star is a white dwarf, a main sequence star or a giant. By the use of this technique it becomes possible to obtain the distance of a very distant star, as long as one can photograph its spectrum and classify it as to spectral type.

5-20 The Mass-Luminosity Relation and the Luminosity Function

The mass-luminosity relation expresses the fact that for the majority of stars the more massive the star the greater is its luminosity. The luminosity increases approximately as the power 3.5 of the mass, which means that a small increase in mass produces a large increase in brightness. The relation holds best for stars on the main sequence of the H-R diagram, fairly well for the giants and not at all for the white dwarfs. The latter are much less luminous than their masses would require them to be.

The luminosity function relates the numbers of stars at each value of the absolute magnitude. The relation shows that the number of stars increases very rapidly as one goes to fainter objects. In a rough way, and to illustrate the extremes involved, there are about 450,000 stars of absolute magnitude +15 for every one of absolute magnitude −5. The function is not too well known because of the problem of statistical sampling. To get a good idea of the number of stars of absolute magnitude −5 it is necessary to use enormous volumes of space, because these stars are so rare. At the other end of the scale the intrinsically faint stars are also apparently faint even when they are close, so that even if one uses a large volume of space they will not be detected.

QUESTIONS

1. Would it be possible for a planet to revolve about the sun just above the photosphere?

2. What are the physical differences between our sun and a type O star? A type M dwarf? A type F white dwarf?

3. If a star whose surface temperature is hotter than that of the sun has the same absolute magnitude in the yellow-green region, will it be brighter or fainter in the ultraviolet region?

4. Why is it not possible to see the solar corona from the earth's surface, except at the time of a total solar eclipse or with a coronagraph?

5. What is the ratio of brightness of two stars whose magnitude difference is 12?

6. Discuss the appearance of the sun as seen by an observer on Pluto.

7. If an observer on Pluto were to see a solar flare, how much time would have elapsed between the occurrence of the flare and the observation on Pluto?

Chapter 6

Variety Among Stars — Stellar Systems

In this chapter we will discuss the extraordinary variety that is found among stars. As we have seen, stars range enormously in temperature, diameter, color, mass and luminosity. Some stars like the sun show no evidence of variation in brightness, while others may change by many magnitudes in a day or two. There are stars that rotate rapidly, and others that seem not to rotate at all. Some systems are double or triple, and many may be in a cluster of hundreds of thousands of stars, or even a galaxy made up of billions of stars.

6-1   Visual Double Stars

About 50,000 double star systems are known whose doubleness can be seen visually with a telescope. The reality of the physical connection of the shorter period systems is revealed by the revolution of the two stars around each other, just as the earth and moon would be seen to do if viewed from another planet. The orbital periods of the visual double stars range from the shortest of 1.7 years to values that may be millions of years. The very long period systems change their relative position so slowly that they are known only from their common proper motion.

Since double stars are gravitationally connected they revolve around each other in an orbit which has a period, an eccentricity, a semi-major axis and an inclination. Because the orbital planes are randomly oriented in space, the orbital motion of one star with respect to the other will be observed in projection on the plane of the sky. The change in apparent separation and position angle can be plotted after one whole revolution, and from this plot one can determine the true shape of the orbit and its semi-major axis in seconds of arc. The latter, if divided by the parallax, will give the semimajor axis in astronomical units. A proper study of the plot will also reveal the true orbital eccentricity, the inclination and the spatial orientation of the major axis.

The most important reason for the study of visual binaries is that they are our main source of stellar masses. Kepler's Third Law in its general form (Sec. 1-15) states that

$$\frac{a^3_{\text{a.u.}}}{P^2_{\text{yrs}}} = (m_1 + m_2)$$

where the unit of mass is that of the sun. When a and P are substituted in this equation the result is the mass sum but not the individual masses. To separate the masses it is necessary to know the mass ratio. This ratio, m_1/m_2, is equal to the ratio d_2/d_1, where d_1 and d_2 are the distances of each star from the center of mass. The position of the center of mass can be obtained from proper motion studies of the binary. The mass center will move in a straight line with constant speed, but the two stars will each revolve about the mass center in a sinuous line back and forth on either side of the mass center. The difficulty in making these measurements is one reason so few individual stellar masses have been determined.

To accumulate the necessary data on a visual binary with a period as long as 100 years, three or four generations of astronomers must observe the object. This exemplifies the type of cooperation that makes possible some kinds of astronomical research.

6-2   Spectroscopic Binaries

If for a given binary one were to keep the mass sum constant and decrease a, then P would also decrease in such a way as to keep a^3/P^2 constant. Algebraic manipulation of the formula to obtain the orbital velocity of one star with respect to another will show that

$$V_{\text{orbital}} = 2\pi \sqrt{\frac{m_1 + m_2}{a}}$$

This shows that as a decreases, the orbital velocity increases. But also, as a decreases it will be harder to see the system as a visual binary. Because the orbital velocity becomes larger it becomes possible to use the Doppler effect to observe periodic changes in the radial velocity, due to the variable projection of the orbital velocity on the line of sight. Figure 6-1 illustrates this point. Here the motion of each star will be considered to be in a circular orbit around the mass center. Let the mass ratio (m_1/m_2) be 2. Then, from what was said in the previous section, $d_2 = 2d_1$ and the circumference of the orbit of m_2 around the mass center will be twice that of m_1. If the orbital velocity of m_1 is 50 mi/sec, then that of m_2 will be 100 mi/sec, since both stars move around in their orbits in the same time; m_1 and m_2 will always be on opposite sides of the mass center.

At positions marked A and a, both stars are moving at right angles to the line of sight and the radial velocity is zero. The same will be true at C and c, half a period later. At position B, the star m_1 will be moving away from the observer with a radial velocity of $+50$ mi/sec, but at the same moment, m_2 will be at position b and will have a radial velocity of -100 mi/sec. At positions D and d half a period later, the magnitude of the velocities will be the same but the algebraic signs will be reversed. In the figure, an intermediate position is shown where the projection of the orbital velocity of m_1 on the line of sight is $+25$ mi/sec and that of m_2 is -50 mi/sec. During one whole period there will be a smooth variation in radial velocity from zero to plus, to zero to minus, and back to zero. The spectrum of each star will shift back and forth from red to violet. When one spectrum

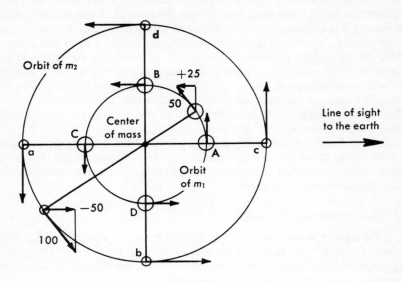

Fig. 6-1. **Illustration of the variable radial velocity of the two components of a spectroscopic binary.**

is shifted to the red the other will be displaced to the violet. It is easy to see that the total velocity range for each star is directly proportional to the size of its orbit and the ratio of the velocity ranges is inversely proportional to the mass ratio. This is true even if the inclination is less than 90 degrees because each velocity range will be decreased by the same factor.

In this particular figure where the inclination is 90 degrees, we can also get the mass sum. (The orbital inclination is measured with respect to the plane of the sky.) Let the half range in the radial velocity (the orbital velocity) of m_1 be called K_1. Then the radius of its orbit (a_1) will be $K_1 \times P/2\pi$, and a corresponding computation for m_2 will give a_2. The sum ($a_1 + a_2$) will give a, the semimajor axis of the orbit of one star with respect to another. The cube of a divided by P^2 in the proper units will give the sum of the masses. Since the mass ratio m_1/m_2 is equal to K_2/K_1, the combination of this value with the mass sum will give the individual masses.

A few hundred spectroscopic binaries are known with periods ranging from a little less than a day to many years. The orbital eccentricities range from practically zero to almost 0.9, although for most cases the value is small. Because of the wide range in period, orbital eccentricity, inclination, spectral type, and diameter of components and their spectral types, this is a richly rewarding field of research. No two spectroscopic binaries are alike. It must be noted here that if the inclination of the orbit is small and the orbital velocities are also small, the range in radial velocity may be too small to be detected, and hence one may be unaware that the star is a binary. A proper treatment of the statistics on spectroscopic binaries demonstrates that about half of all the stars are binaries.

6-3 Eclipsing Binaries

From what has been said in the last section, it will be apparent that when the inclination is 90 degrees (or close to that figure), we shall also have an *eclipsing binary,* and there will be two eclipses in one revolution when both stars are on the line joining the center of mass to the observer. From measures of brightness throughout a complete revolution, a light curve is obtained. A suitable analysis of this light curve will reveal a great deal about the system. To illustrate, let star A in Fig. 6-2 be the smaller with one-third the radius of B and one-ninth of its surface area, and let each star contribute one-half of the total light of the system. First of all, picture A being eclipsed by the larger star B. As pictured in Fig. 6-2 there will be four contacts as A moves from left to right. Since the orbital inclination is 90 degrees and B is larger than A, at mid-eclipse the eclipse will be total and central. The resulting light curve is shown in Fig. 6-2 and the times of the four contacts are indicated. Outside of the eclipse the total light is 100% and the light curve is flat; that is, the light is constant. The light curve is not a straight line between first and second contacts or between third and fourth

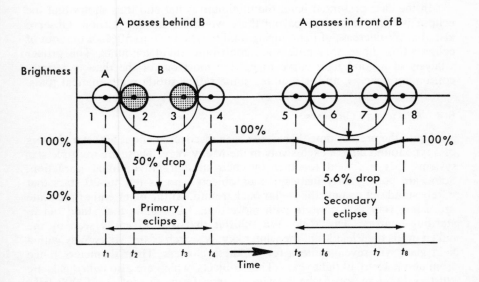

Fig. 6-2. **The contacts and the light curve of an eclipsing binary.**

contacts because the rate at which B covers A is not constant. (It is assumed that both stars are uniformly bright over their whole surfaces.)

Note that $t_2 - t_1$ is the time for the leading edge of B to cover the diameter of A, and that it is equal to $t_4 - t_3$. The interval $t_3 - t_1$ is the time required for the left-hand edge of A to cross the diameter of B. This time interval is also equal to $t_4 - t_2$. Let V be the circular orbital velocity of B with respect to A. A little thought will show that the radius of A (r_A) equals $V(t_2 - t_1)/2$ or $V(t_4 - t_3)/2$. For the same reasons, r_B equals $V(t_3 - t_1)/2$ or $V(t_4 - t_2)/2$. Furthermore, the radius of the orbit of B around A is equal to its circumference divided by 2π or $(V \times P)/2\pi$, which we may call R. Now, even if we do not know V, we can obtain the relative sizes of each star with respect to the separation (R) between them. Therefore, $r_A/R = \pi(t_2 - t_1)/P$ and $r_B = \pi(t_3 - t_1)/P$. As an example let the former be equal to 0.2 and the latter 0.4. Then the radius of A occupies 0.2 of the separation R and B occupies 0.4 of R. This shows that the separation of their surfaces is 1.0 − (0.2 + 0.4), or 0.4 of the separation, and that the two stars are far from being in contact. Now if V was known from spectroscopic evidence one could get, as seen above, the actual radii of the two components and their actual separation. The four contacts and the shape of the light curve at secondary eclipse are shown in Fig. 6-2. The depth of the minimum is only $\frac{1}{9}$ of 50 percent. The analysis is too complicated to be shown here, but if the light curve is an accurate one it is possible to show whether or not the stars are spherical and to obtain the orbital inclination plus the degree to which the stars are uniformly bright over their whole surfaces.

In the case presented here, the minimum is flat and thus shows that the eclipse is total. If it were partial there would be no flat portion. Observe also that the decrease of light during totality was down to 50% of that out of eclipse; this shows that both stars contribute equal amounts. The proper analysis of a good light curve to get the most out of the data is a time-consuming process, and it requires some rather subtle mathematical tools.

6-4   Milky Way Clusters

Up to the present time there have been discovered about 500 star clusters of a type found almost exclusively in the Milky Way. These are multiple star systems that are held together by their mutual gravitational attraction. Some are poor, rather inconspicuous objects with as few as 20 stars that barely stand out against the stellar background. At the other end of the scale are a few very rich clusters with more than 1,000 stars that stand out in startling contrast. The Milky Way cluster that is most easily seen by the naked eye is the Pleiades in the winter sky. A search of the Milky Way with a field glass will reveal quite a few of these clusters. Their diameters range from about 15 to 40 light years. These objects, which are also called galactic clusters for a reason to be seen later, may be as distant as 15,000 light years—at such distances the angular diameter of the cluster is so small and its stars so faint that the object merges into the rich Milky Way background.

Fig. 6-3. **A Milky Way, or galactic, star cluster. (Photograph from the Mount Wilson and Palomar Observatories.)**

6-5 Globular Clusters

A cluster of an entirely different type is called a *globular cluster* because of its compact, round appearance. More than 100 are known. They are found all over the sky and do not favor the Milky Way. The remarkable feature of these objects is that the number of cluster members ranges from a few thousand to perhaps as much as one million. When seen in a telescope or on a photographic plate, the star images near the cluster center are so tightly packed together that they cannot be seen as individuals. The diameters of globular clusters range from about 75 light years to perhaps as much as 400. Their distances from the sun range from about 30,000 light years to over 300,000. The determination of their distances will be discussed in a later section.

It is clear that there is a great difference between these two types of clusters. Their origins and past histories must be quite different. These topics will be discussed later on in this chapter.

Fig. 6-4. **The bright globular cluster in the constellation Hercules. (Photograph from the Mount Wilson and Palomar Observatories.)**

INTRINSICALLY VARIABLE STARS

Tens of thousands of stars have been discovered that are intrinsically variable. It appears that in almost all cases their light changes are the result of changes in size and temperature. The change in light may be as small as can be detected or up to many magnitudes. For some of these variables, the light changes are closely periodic and of constant brightness range, but for others the changes are quite erratic. This is a rich field for research. This discussion will be limited to two types, the Cepheid variables and the novae.

6-6   Cepheid Variables

Cepheids (seph'-ee-ids) are pulsating stars whose light variations result from a change in surface area and surface temperature. There is actually a change in spectral type during each cycle of variation. For the great majority of Cepheids, the time from one light maximum to the next is closely constant, although in a very few well observed cases slow period changes have been detected. To a large extent, the shape of the light curve and the range of brightness are the same from one cycle to the next. The two main classes of cepheids are discussed below.

Classical Cepheids

These variables have periods that range from about 2 to 50 days. A typical period is about a week. The typical light range is about one magnitude. A typical spectral type is from G2 at minimum to F2 at maximum. Radial velocity observations confirm the pulsation. The mean absolute magnitude extends over the range from -2 to -6. These are luminous giants.

Short Period Cepheids

These variables have some resemblances to the classical Cepheids except that their periods are shorter, their brightness range is less and they are intrinsically fainter. They are also called *cluster* Cepheids because they are often found in globular clusters, but not in Milky Way clusters. However, a few Milky Way clusters do have one or two classical Cepheids among their member stars. The range of period for the cluster Cepheids is from 0.1 day to nearly one day. The average magnitude range is a little less than one magnitude. Their spectral type is around A and F and their mean absolute magnitude is close to $+0.5$.

6-7   The Period-Luminosity Relation

One of the most useful discoveries in astronomy was made in 1917 when it was observed that there is a good correlation between the periods and the absolute magnitudes of the classical Cepheids. This relationship is called the Period-Luminosity Relation and it is illustrated in Fig. 6-5. In this figure, the absolute magnitude is plotted against the period on a logarithmic scale. Observe that the classical Cepheids are confined to a rather narrow band and that the longer the period, the brighter the variable. The short period Cepheids are also plotted on this diagram but there is no change in absolute magnitude with period. Note that the cluster Cepheids continue on the diagram into a band called Population II Cepheids, and not on into the band of the classical Cepheids which are of type Population I. The meaning of "population" will be discussed at the end of this chapter.

This relation can be used to find the distance of a cluster of stars if one of its members is either kind of Cepheid. If it is a classical Cepheid it is necessary to determine first its period by observation and also its average apparent magnitude. From the Period-Luminosity Relation one obtains the absolute magnitude and then the distance modulus $m - M$, which then gives the distance as described in Sec. 5-15. If the variable is identified as a short period Cepheid, we need only to know that its absolute magnitude is $+0.5$; we can then proceed in the same way. The variable can be put in its proper class from the shape of the light curve and the knowledge that the short period Cepheids have periods less than a day and the classical type have periods longer than one day. The cluster Cepheids in the globular clusters have given the distances of these clusters. Since the classical Cepheids are much brighter objects, they may be used to determine far greater distances such as those of galaxies. (Galaxies will be treated in the next chapter.)

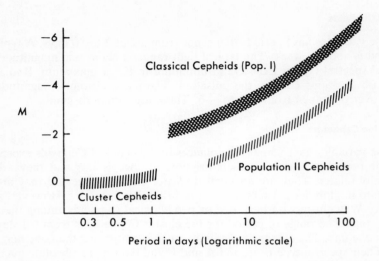

Fig. 6-5. **The period-lumosity relation for Cepheid variable stars.**

6-8   The Novae: Ordinary and Super

A nova (new star) is the most startling of all variable stars. It is a star which without warning increases its brightness many magnitudes in a few days, and then slowly (and sometimes irregularly) fades away to about its pre-outburst brightness. The period of fading may require several years. The average *ordinary* nova will increase its brightness about ten magnitudes in three or four days. The decrease is often accompanied by rapid fluctuations which may be periodic for a time. The average ordinary nova will reach an M of -6 to -8—a very luminous object. An ordinary nova is a rare event. Statistical studies show that 20 to 30 occur in our galaxy per year. Even more rarely is such an object near enough to reach naked eye visibility, and most are found on photographic plates taken for other purposes.

Spectroscopic observations during the outburst reveal that there is a very rapid expansion of the star's outer layers. Expansion velocities as high as 1500 mi/sec have been observed; these must in every case be greater than the escape velocity from the star. The whole star is not blowing up, but only an outer shell, and the mass loss is probably not greater than 1%. There is some evidence that some novae repeat this process after an interval of a decade or so. It has been observed that within some months or years after the outburst of an ordinary nova, sometimes a shell or ring forms around the faded image of the nova. This appears to be the nova's shell of ejected material which has grown to such an angular diameter as to become visible.

A *supernova* is an exceptionally violent phenomenon which is much more rare than an ordinary nova. The increase in brightness may be as much as 20 magnitudes. The absolute magnitude at maximum brightness averages about −17 but it ranges from −14 to −20. Supernovae are often observed in other galaxies, and studies show that in an average galaxy they occur perhaps once every few hundred years. The mass loss in such an explosion is at least 10% and in some cases it may even be total.

Very little is known about the reason for a nova's outburst. It appears that something has gone wrong with the process of nuclear energy generation in the star.

6-9 The Crab Nebula

No supernovae have been observed in our celestial neighborhood since the time of modern astronomical instruments, but there are old records of a few. In the constellation Taurus is found the Crab Nebula, a diffuse, bright nebulosity shown in Fig. 6-6. This nebula is known to be expanding. From its expansion rate and its present size, astronomers computed, earlier in this century, that the expansion began about the year A.D. 1050. A search of old

Fig. 6-6. The Crab Nebula. (Photograph from the Mount Wilson and Palomar Observatories.)

records finally revealed a Chinese source that reported the appearance in A.D. 1054 of an exceedingly bright new star very nearly in that part of the sky now occupied by the Crab Nebula. Astronomers are convinced that the two objects are the same and that the star observed in China was a supernova. The Crab Nebula is a strong emitter of radio noise. Several other galactic nebulae are thought to be the remnants of supernova explosions.

6-10   Our Galaxy: The Milky Way

Galileo first observed that the number of stars seen with his telescope was much greater in the Milky Way than in directions away from it. This simple observation (made more than 350 years ago) has had a great influence on the course of astronomy. This band of light around the sky was revealed to be a zone of great numbers of stars too faint to be resolved by the naked eye. When a telescope is moved perpendicular to the Milky Way, many more stars are seen in that region than above or below it. When the telescope is moved along the Milky Way, the number of stars seen in the field of view fluctuates a good deal; the richest region is in the Sagittarius area of the southern Milky Way, and the least rich is in that part of the band 180 degrees away in the northern sky.

The interpretation of these observations that has emerged after three and one-half centuries is that our sun (the place of observation) is in a large, flattened cluster of stars, and that our position in the cluster is quite a bit off center. This system of stars is called *the galaxy*. There are many other galaxies in the space beyond our own (see Chapter 7). Figure 6-7 is a schematic view of our galaxy as seen from the edge. It is seen to be quite flattened and with a central bulge. Seen from above or below it would be roughly circular in outline, with spiral arms trailing out from the central nucleus. See Figs. 7-1 and 7-2 in the next chapter for galaxies similar to our own.

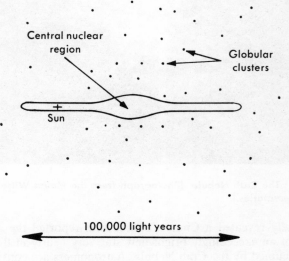

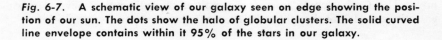

Fig. 6-7.   **A schematic view of our galaxy seen on edge showing the position of our sun. The dots show the halo of globular clusters. The solid curved line envelope contains within it 95% of the stars in our galaxy.**

The total number of stars in our galaxy is about 100 billion, and this figure is also its approximate mass in solar units. Its diameter is about 100,000 light years. This means that if a nova were to burst out on one edge of our galaxy, an observer on the opposite edge would not be aware of it for 100,000 years. Our sun is about 30,000 light years from the center. The thickness of our galaxy in the neighborhood of the sun is about 2,000 light years.

Although the galaxy is held together by the mutual gravitation of its stars, its high degree of flattening is the result of rapid rotation. Most of the stars appear to be revolving about the center in nearly circular orbits. Within about 20,000 light years from the center the thick, dense nuclear region seems to be rotating more or less like a solid, but beyond this the orbital velocities decrease with distance from the center as the planets do in our solar system. At our distance from the galactic center the orbital velocity is about 180 mi/sec and the period of revolution is close to 200 million years.

6-11 The Interstellar Medium

Although the patchiness of the Milky Way can be observed by the naked eye, the detailed structure is only revealed by large scale photographs covering about 100 square degrees, as in Fig. 6-8. A typical photograph will show great differences in the number of stars per square degree. This non-uniformity is caused almost entirely by huge clouds of interstellar dust and gas. This material is very strongly concentrated toward the plane of the Milky Way (the galactic plane) and in the spiral arms. All the space in our

Fig. 6-8. Bright and dark nebulosities in the Milky Way in the constellation Monoceros. (Photograph from the Mount Wilson and Palomar Observatories.)

galaxy is pervaded by this medium, but there are large variations in its density. The more obvious, obscuring patches result from the larger, closer and denser clouds, some of which are so dense as to reduce the brightness of the stars behind them by more than five magnitudes.

Most of the gas between the much denser clouds consists of hydrogen atoms with a density of about one per cubic centimeter, but other chemical elements are also present in much smaller numbers. For about every 1,000 hydrogen atoms there is probably one dust particle with a diameter of 10^{-5} centimeters (1,000 Å) or less. The dust and gas occur together and the total mass of the dust is about 1% of the whole medium. In spite of the relative scarcity of the dust particles they are the main contributors to the obscuration of light. The total mass of the interstellar material is much less than that material in the form of stars. Even in the thickest parts of the clouds the density is still so low as to constitute a very high vacuum by laboratory standards.

6-12   The Evidence For The Instellar Medium

Interstellar Reddening

It has been known for a long time that star colors become progressively redder for the fainter and more distant stars. The interstellar material, particularly the dust, scatters the starlight out of the beam coming to the observer and causes it to appear fainter than it would otherwise be. The scattering is greater for the shorter blue wavelengths than for the red, with the result that a very distant blue O or B type star may appear red. This reddening is quite small at a few hundred light years but becomes important for distances of much more than 1,000 light years. For distances in the galactic plane greater than about 15,000 light years we can scarcely see any stars because of this obscuration. In fact our direct view of the galaxy is quite limited and is confined in the galactic plane to our rather immediate neighborhood. As soon as one looks in directions somewhat above or below the galactic plane (i.e., beyond the band of the Milky Way) the obscuration is greatly reduced because the obscuring material is so closely confined to the galactic plane.

Bright Nebulae

Among the darker, absorbing regions are often found bright nebulae of considerable extent which are associated with dark nebulae. These are explained by the presence near to, or even within, the dark material of very hot, bright stars which illuminate a portion of the dark nebulosity. The famous Orion Nebula is a good example. (See also Fig. 6-8). If the illuminating star is very hot, its copius ultraviolet radiation will excite and ionize the gases in the cloud so that the spectrum of the bright nebula is a bright line (emission) spectrum characteristic of the elements of the gas. If the star is too cool, the excitation will be small and the spectrum will be much like that of the illuminating star reflected from the dust and gas.

Interstellar Absorption Lines

Among the numerous examples of spectroscopic binaries are some with type O and B components which, although they may be quite distant, are bright enough to have their spectra recorded photographically. Most of the stellar lines are broad and change their wavelengths with the orbital period, but for the more distant binaries there are usually found a few narrow absorption lines of constant radial velocity. The most common of these are identified with neutral and singly ionized calcium, iron and sodium. These sharp lines were once thought to be produced in an extended, stationary atmosphere around the binary until it was found that their strength increased with the distance of the binary. The most obvious explanation is that these lines are produced by absorption in the space between the binary and ourselves. Quite commonly these sharp lines are multiple, a fact which is explained by assuming that each component is produced by a separate cloud and that the wavelength separation of the components is due to the different radial velocities of the clouds.

The Radio Emission of Interstellar Hydrogen

Just after World War II it was predicted, and soon observed, that atomic hydrogen in interstellar space is emitting a single emission line with a wavelength of a little more than 21 centimeters (1420 megacycles/sec). It is possible to detect neutral hydrogen clouds at very great distances in the Milky Way plane and to map their positions even beyond the galactic center to the opposite edge of the galaxy. As we said previously, observations in the optical region do not extend beyond about 15,000 light years from the sun. The results show that there are great arms of hydrogen clouds spiralling out from the galactic center and that these arms contain the great proportion of the stars in our galaxy. Our sun is in one of the spiral arms.

6-13   The Formation of Stars

Scattered about in many parts of the Milky Way, and particularly in regions of heavy obscuration, are large numbers of small dark *globules* of dense interstellar matter which are thought to be in the process of condensing to form stars. Rough measurements suggest for these globules masses sufficient to form a single star, a binary or even a star cluster. Theory suggests that there is an upper limit to the mass of a star and, in fact, none are known with masses more than 100 times that of our sun. The relative scarcity of very massive stars suggests that smaller masses are preferred. If the mass of the globule is greater than 100 solar masses, then at least two stars will be formed. Present theory proposes that as the globule becomes smaller under its own gravitational attraction, its temperature increases by the transfer of gravitational energy to the thermal (kinetic) energy of the gas. At an early stage in this process the star will have a low surface temperature, a color and a faint absolute magnitude which would place it far to the right and very much below the lower right-hand corner of the H-R diagram. As contraction proceeds both its surface temperature and its luminosity will increase until finally it enters the boundaries of the H-R diagram. From here it will proceed to that point on the main sequence that is appropriate to its mass. Its movement across the H-R diagram, ending on the main sequence, is very rapid. By this time its central temperature is so high that it is able to support the nuclear reactions which are discussed in the next section.

6-14   Nuclear Reactions in Stars and Stellar Evolution

This is an extensive and important topic which we can only mention briefly here. Only nuclear reactions can provide the energy output of stars that will keep them shining for billions of years. For the majority of stars this is a reaction by which hydrogen is converted into helium. The resultant mass loss appears as radiant energy and thermal energy. This process takes place only at temperatures of many millions of degrees. Such temperatures are found in the central cores of stars. Because hydrogen is such an abundant element in stars and the conversion to helium of even a small quantity of hydrogen produces such a large amount of energy, this process can furnish energy for a very long time.

When a star, regardless of mass, reaches the main sequence on the H-R diagram, it has begun to "burn" its hydrogen by converting it to helium. However, some of the blue supergiants with luminosities greater than one million times that of the sun are consuming their hydrogen just that much faster. It is true that the mass of the blue supergiant is greater, but usually by not much more than 40 or 50 times. One must conclude that these highly luminous objects are evolving and aging very rapidly, and that they must be very young in years as compared to the sun.

As the star uses up its hydrogen, it slowly leaves the main sequence and moves upward and to the right in the H-R diagram toward the region of the redder giant stars. The rate at which it does so depends on its mass. A type M main sequence dwarf will probably stay on the main sequence for many billions of years before it moves up appreciably; but a type B or O star would move an appreciable distance upward in a few million years. This can be seen quite easily when the spectral types (or temperatures) and absolute magnitudes of galactic cluster stars are plotted on the H-R diagram. Presumably all the cluster stars formed from a large globule at very nearly the same time and all are of nearly the same age. If the brighter members of the cluster are type O and B stars, it is seen that they have already left the main sequence and are above it while the faintest and least massive members much farther down the main sequence fit closely to that sequence.

Theory suggests that as the hydrogen becomes exhausted in the central core, the core contracts under gravitational contraction and the core temperature increases. At a very elevated temperature, the helium becomes hot enough so that it can be converted into heavier elements with a release of additional nuclear energy. At this point, the star is past middle age. At some time during this phase, the star may become unstable and pulsate with a variation in brightness. In some instances it may even become a nova. The actual details of the evolutionary track on the H-R diagram are fairly complex and are much influenced by the star's mass.

After the star has used up the nuclear energy sources in the heavier elements, there is no fuel left. Quite rapidly it begins to contract and become fainter. In some cases it may cross the main sequence going downward and become a member of the white dwarf sequence well below the main sequence. As seen in Section 5-18, most of these stars are not much larger than the earth and have masses comparable to the sun, their densities are enormous. At this stage, the star shines only by its internal heat since no nuclear sources are left. Because its radiating surface is small compared with its mass and high heat content per pound, it will cool very slowly over a time of several tens of billions of years and end as a black dwarf. For more details on the whole process of stellar evolution, see the references given in the appendix.

6-15 The Galactic Halo

Almost all of the matter in our galaxy (such as single stars, binaries, star clusters and interstellar matter) is closely confined to the highly flattened system. However, the globular clusters and other types of stars (such as the short period Cepheids) are not confined to the galactic plane, but are a part of the *galactic halo*. This halo of clusters and individual stars forms another system in addition to the flattened one. The space distribution of the globular clusters is nearly spherical, with its center at the galactic center itself. The evidence strongly suggests that the globular clusters revolve about the galactic center in highly elliptical orbits with inclinations of all values. Under these conditions a globular cluster which is now high above the galactic plane will in time pass once again around and close to the galactic nucleus; in so doing it will pass through the flattened system. The chance of a star collision is very small.

The globular clusters contain no interstellar clouds. The reason may be that as the cluster passes through the flattened system its interstellar clouds collide with the clouds in the flattened system and are left behind. Because the globular clusters have no interstellar clouds, no stars are being formed in them.

6-16 Stellar Population Types

Since about 1945 it has become apparent that there are distinct differences between the proportions of the chemical elements in stars. It is now known that most of the stars in the flattened system of the galaxy are relatively rich in the heavier elements, as compared with the galactic halo stars such as the globular cluster stars. Stars are still forming out of the dust and gas clouds in the spiral arms, but there is no such material in the globular clusters and no new stars are forming in them. The stars in the spiral arms are mainly Population I objects while those in the halo are Population II objects. It is now believed that the globular clusters are very old objects that formed out of nearly pure hydrogen. In the galactic plane, where the novae are concentrated, a nova occasionally explodes and returns to the interstellar medium some of its material; this material is quite rich in the heavier elements produced by nuclear reactions during the star's lifetime. New stars forming out of this enriched medium will have quite a different initial chemical composition than those formed from nearly pure hydrogen, which is believed to be the primordial substance. Physical considerations too complex to be discussed here show that a star's evolution over the ages will depend to a considerable extent on the heavy element proportion of the material from which the star was formed. Such differences in structure are actually observed. As examples, the classical Cepheids are Population I objects and the short period Cepheids belong to Population II. Our sun is a Population I object. It should be easy to see that classification into just two categories is an oversimplification, and that there ought to be a range all the way from stars with a small proportion of heavy elements to stars with a high proportion. Just why the concentration toward the galactic plane should be correlated with heavy element abundance is not at all clear—it is a fruitful subject for future study.

QUESTIONS

1. What is the sum of the masses of the two components of a double star if the period is two centuries and the separation is 7 billion miles?
2. What effects would you expect to observe in the light curve of an eclipsing binary if one of the stars had a large sun spot like those on our sun?
3. What might be expected to happen in our solar system if our sun became an ordinary nova? A supernova?
4. What changes would be observed in the light curve of an eclipsing binary if the stars were so close together that the two surfaces facing each other were made hotter than the opposite surfaces?
5. Suppose that a globular cluster has a diameter of 20 light years and contains 100,000 stars whose average diameter is that of our sun. What fraction of the projected area of the cluster would be covered by the discs of the stars? Note that the chance that one star in the cluster would eclipse another would be small.
6. What is the difference in absolute magnitude of two stars of types B and K when both are on the main sequence?
7. What is the absolute magnitude of a type I Cepheid if it has a pulsation period of ten days?
8. None of the stars in the sky that are visible to the unaided eye are type M main sequence stars. Suggest a reason for this.

Chapter 7

Galaxies and Cosmology

Beginning with the use of large telescopes about 200 years ago, and particularly with the advent of photography somewhat less than a century ago, astronomers have discovered a large number of nebulous objects that are *not* confined to the Milky Way region, as are those bright nebulae that we now know are associated with the interstellar clouds. Photography has revealed these nebulous objects all over the sky. Most of them show a rather symmetrical structure, in contrast to the bright nebulae in the Milky Way which are irregular in outline. Many of these symmetrical objects show a bright nucleus from which emerge spiral arms. Others look like bright globules that are circular or elliptical in outline. When counts were made of the number of these objects per square degree down to a given limiting magnitude, almost none were found in the Milky Way. Outside of this region the number per square degree increased steadily, reaching a maximum at the poles of the Milky Way. Good photographs of the spiral nebulae show that they are probably flattened, disc-shaped objects with a random spatial orientation, so that they are observed on edge at one extreme and in plane at the other.

Among these spiral nebulae the Great Nebula in the constellation Andromeda has the greatest angular diameter. This elliptically shaped spiral has an angular diameter of five degrees along its major axis. The bright, central nuclear region is just visible to the naked eye; this spiral nebula is the only one that can be seen without a telescope. The outer spiral region has a surface brightness much less than that of the central nucleus and can be seen only on long exposure photographs, as in Fig. 7-1.

7-1 The Distance of the Andromeda Galaxy

These galaxies were first thought to be objects in our own galaxy. Many astronomers believed them to be rapidly rotating gaseous masses. However, about 1920, Mount Wilson Observatory astronomers resolved the outer portions of the Andromeda Nebula into stars and showed that this object is really an asemblage or kind of cluster of stars. In 1924 Edwin Hubble of that observatory identified a few of these stars as classical Cepheids with a mean apparent magnitude of about $+18$. Continued observations accumulated

Fig. 7-1. **The spiral galaxy in the constellation Andromeda and its two companion galaxies. (Photograph from the Mount Wilson and Palomar Observatories.)**

enough data to obtain the period of the light variation. By means of the Period-Luminosity Relation discussed in Chapter 6, Hubble was able to calculate for the first time the distance of a spiral nebula. The modern value for the distance of the Andromeda Nebula is about 2.2 million light years; therefore it is well outside the confines of our galaxy. Hubble determined distances for a number of the brighter galaxies which indicated that the Andromeda galaxy is the nearest spiral.

This galaxy is nearly the twin of our own—it has nearly the same linear diameter, mass and luminosity. Like our own, it has spiral arms and interstellar clouds. Careful studies reveal that the resolved stars in the outer spiral arms are very bright blue stars of Population II like those in our own spiral arms. It is possible to observe Milky Way type clusters in the spiral arms and to see that the Andromeda galaxy has a halo of globular clusters like our own. Occasionally, ordinary novae are seen. Radial velocity studies show that this galaxy is in rotation.

7-2   *The Classification of Galaxies*

It has been clear for some time that the elliptical and spiral nebulae are really galaxies in their own right. They are, in fact, gigantic assemblages of stars. At one time it was fashionable to call them island universes. Of all these galaxies the Andromeda galaxy is the nearest however, there are two companions to our own galaxy called the Magellanic Clouds which are classified as galaxies but are much smaller than our own. Each of these dwarf galaxies is about 200,000 light years from the center of our galaxy. They are seen close to the south celestial pole and hence are not seen in middle northern latitudes.

Galaxies may be classed by their appearance into three groups: spiral, elliptical and irregular. About 75% are spirals, 21% ellipticals and the remainder irregulars.

The spiral galaxies have a nucleus from which the spiral arms (usually two) emerge. When the nucleus is relatively large, the arms are tightly wound around the nucleus; but if the nucleus is comparatively small the arms are spread out and rather diffuse. Bright and dark nebulae are found in the arms together with blue giants of Population I. No doubt all the other stars on the main sequence are present, but they are too faint to be resolved. With our present telescopic equipment an astronomer in the Andromeda galaxy could not resolve our sun. When a spiral is seen from the edge, the dark nebulae form an obscuring band along the whole length of the galaxy, as in Fig. 7-2. Examples of spirals with large and small nuclei are shown in Figs. 7-3 and 7-4. Among the spirals is a subclass called the barred spirals, an example of which is shown in Fig. 7-5. The barred spirals show a nucleus, through which passes a straight, luminous bar; from each end of the bar a spiral arm begins.

The *elliptical* galaxies are spherical or elliptical in outline, as shown in Fig. 7-6. They are distinguished by having no spiral arms. Only rarely

Fig. 7-2. **A spiral galaxy seen on edge. (Photograph from the Mount Wilson and Palomar Observatories.)**

Fig. 7-3. A spiral galaxy with a relatively small central nucleus. (Photograph from the Mount Wilson and Palomar Observatories.)

Fig. 7-4. A spiral galaxy with a relatively large nucleus. (Photograph from the Mount Wilson and Palomar Observatories.)

Fig. 7-5. A barred spiral galaxy. (Photograph from the Mount Wilson and Palomar Observatories.)

Fig. 7-6. An elliptical galaxy. (Photograph from the Mount Wilson and Palomar Observatories.)

does one see any interstellar material in this type of galaxy. This should mean that stars are no longer being born in the elliptical galaxies, and indeed the brighter stars are red giants of Population II. In this respect the elliptical galaxies resemble the nuclei of spirals, whose brightest stars are also of Population II.

The least numerous class of galaxies is the *irregular* type. Irregulars exhibit no symmetry of form or plan.

7-3   The Determination of the Distances to Galaxies

The use of the classical Cepheids to determine the distances to galaxies applies only to the nearer ones in which the Cepheids are bright enough to be resolved as individual stars. Beyond this, the problem becomes very difficult and less direct.

One method that applies fairly well to galaxies near enough to be resolved into stars is to determine the apparent magnitude of the brightest, blue supergiant stars and to assume that their mean absolute magnitude is the same as that of such objects in our own galaxy, for which we have information on absolute magnitude. The same technique applies to galaxies whose globular clusters can be sampled. Similarly, the astronomer can study the apparent magnitudes of the galaxy's ordinary novae and once again assume that their mean absolute magnitude is the same as for those in our galaxy. The difference between the mean apparent magnitude and the mean absolute magnitude of each class of object gives the distance modulus and hence the distance. The agreement for these classes of objects is good.

However, when it is impossible to resolve these classes of objects in a more distant galaxy, the methods of measurement become more difficult and uncertain. A technique that can be used is to make an estimate of the absolute magnitude of the whole galaxy and obtain the distance modulus from direct measurement of the apparent magnitude. The absolute magnitudes of nearby galaxies can be obtained with some precision because their distances are well known by other methods. The difficulty lies in the wide dispersion of the absolute magnitudes of galaxies taken without regard to class. The dispersion is much less if one regards only the larger spirals and uses them as standards. However, the image of a faint, distant galaxy is so diffuse that it may not be possible to tell to which class of galaxy it belongs. The difficulty may have been somewhat overstated here, but suffice it to say that methods have been derived by those who work in this field and that they give reasonably accurate distances. There are still many pitfalls and the astronomers concerned are far from being satisfied with the present methods for very distant galaxies. As we shall see later the problem of the structure and origin of the universe may well hinge on the accurate measurement of the distances of the most remote galaxies, just where the distances become so uncertain.

7-4   The Absolute Magnitudes, Dimensions and Masses of Galaxies

From the apparent magnitude and the distance of a galaxy one can determine its absolute magnitude. It appears that on the whole the spirals, with a mean M of -21, are the brightest galaxies. A few of the ellipticals are brighter but their mean M is a little less. At the other end of the brightness scale are some of the dwarfs with M around -10, which is about equivalent to that of the brightest blue giants.

Again, the spirals are the largest galaxies, with diameters between 100,000 and 125,000 light years. Some of the dwarfs are no more than about 3,000 light years across. Our knowledge of the number of dwarf galaxies in space is poor because they are so faint that only those nearby can be observed.

Masses of galaxies are hard to determine but some success has been achieved. The method is based on Kepler's Third Law, and the formula is $a^3/P^2 = m_1 + m_2$. First let us consider our own galaxy. We know that most of the mass is concentrated inside our galactic orbit and that its radius is about 30,000 light years. This distance expressed in astronomical units will be a in the formula. The circular orbital velocity of our sun about the galactic center is about 180 mi/sec. This value coupled with the radius a gives an orbital period of about 200 million years. By substituting these values of a and P in the formula, we obtain around 200 billion solar masses for the mass of our galaxy plus that of our sun. The mass outside our orbit may be regarded as too small to make much difference in the total.

For another galaxy, we will select one somewhat inclined from the edge-on position and determine *with respect to the center* of that galaxy the radial velocity of a number of points along the major axis, or apparent diameter, of the projected image of the galaxy. When these velocities are corrected for a constant factor to take into account the inclination, they become *orbital* velocities around the center of that galaxy. If the distance to the galaxy is known and the angular distance has been measured from the center to each point on the axis where a radial velocity was obtained, one may then construct a graph of orbital velocity against distance from the center in light years or astronomical units. With this data we use the same method described for our galaxy in the last paragraph. It is well to pick a good velocity point well outside the nucleus and as close to the edge of the galaxy as possible, in order to ignore the mass outside that radius. This method shows the Andromeda galaxy's mass to be nearly the same as our own. Other methods show that the mass of some of the dwarf galaxies is not much more than that of a million suns.

7-5 Clusters of Galaxies. The Local Group

The evidence is now strong that perhaps all galaxies may be members of clusters of galaxies. The larger of these clusters contain thousands of galaxies, and tend to be very compact. Clusters with a small number of members have a somewhat irregular appearance. There are quite a number of pairs of galaxies. They are so much more numerous than would be expected on the basis of a random distribution on the celestial sphere of single galaxies that one can only assume that they are real physical pairs, in the sense that they revolve about each other. The periods of revolution are so long that no change in radial velocity is observed in a lifetime, but for many of the pairs, the radial velocity is not the same for both galaxies of a pair. In this sense the members of the pair behave like the components of a spectroscopic binary, and from this information it is possible to derive some information on the sum of the masses of the pair.

For a number of nearby clusters in which the galaxies are fairly bright, the radial velocities of a large number of the cluster members have been measured. In any one cluster there is a large range, or spread, in the individual radial velocities of the different members. This range may be 1,000 mi/sec or more. This indicates that there are internal motions in the cluster and that these motions are the result of the gravitational attraction of the members on each other. The spread of these motions around the average can be used to make an estimate of the mass of the whole cluster.

Our galaxy, the Andromeda galaxy, and 15 others are known to be members of what is called the *local cluster* of galaxies. This cluster has a diameter of about 3 million light years. Of these 17 galaxies, 3 are spirals, 10 are ellipticals of all sizes and 4 are irregular galaxies. Six of the ellipticals are classed as dwarfs. The two Magellanic Clouds mentioned earlier are classed as irregulars. Other dwarfs probably are present in this cluster but they may be too faint to be distinguished against the foreground stars in our galaxy, particularly in the Milky Way region. The discovery of large numbers of dwarf galaxies might well change our ideas of the mass density of the universe.

7-6   Intergalactic Matter

To arrive at the mean mass density of the universe it is necessary to know if there is an appreciable amount of intergalactic matter that is not a part of the galaxies themselves. This important problem has led to a great deal of discussion and disagreement. Any intergalactic dust would contribute to the dimming of the more distant galaxies and thereby produce an erroneous increase in their distance determinations. There are probably stars wandering around loose in the vast spaces between the galaxies, since once in a while stars must escape from a galaxy if their velocities are large enough. If, as generally believed, the galaxies condensed out of gas in a very early stage of their evolution there ought to be some gas left, particularly in the clusters of galaxies. Because there are internal motions among the galaxies in a cluster there ought occasionally to be collisions between galaxies. Since the star density in a galaxy is very low it would be possible for one galaxy to pass right through another with scarcely a single stellar collision, but the interstellar clouds in each galaxy would collide and be left behind after the galaxies had separated. The interstellar matter would soon disperse and become intergalactic matter. In the rich, dense clusters there seems to be a dearth of spirals compared to clusters less dense. It is in these dense clusters that one would expect the highest collision rate.

One interesting bit of indirect evidence for intergalactic matter in clusters comes from the study of internal motions. Just as a strong spring will oscillate more rapidly than a weak one, so should the internal motions be greater in a massive cluster than in one less massive. Therefore, it is reasonable to expect that a measurement of the radial velocity spread of the individual cluster members will yield a determination of the mass of the cluster. The mass so determined is much greater than the mass estimated from the counts of galaxies in that cluster. The missing mass could be accounted for either by a large number of dwarf galaxies too faint to be seen or by a large amount of intergalactic dust and gas, or both.

One direct observation of intergalactic matter has been made: not infrequently one can find pairs of galaxies that are well separated by a luminous bridge between them. Possibly these are pairs of galaxies seen not long after a collision, although this is not the only possible explanation. As the galaxies separate, the bridge of gas will disperse to the space between them.

7-7 The Velocity-Distance Relation. The Red Shift

About 1915, astronomers began to obtain spectra of a number of the brighter galaxies within reach of existing telescopes. These spectra are the integrated spectra of a large number of stars in the galaxy. Because of internal motions in the galaxy, most of the fainter, stellar absorption lines are smeared out due to different Doppler shifts. However, some of the stronger lines show—for example, the H and K lines of singly ionized calcium at the respective wavelengths of 3,969 Å and 3,934 Å. Galaxies with bright interstellar clouds show, in addition, a number of emission lines.

Radial velocity measurements of these spectra show that, except for the local cluster, all of the spectra are shifted toward the *red* region of the spectrum. The only reasonable explanation of these red shifts is that they result from velocities of recession. More than that, it quickly became apparent that the recessional velocities are greater for the fainter galaxies than for the brighter ones. Therefore, the recessional velocities increase with the distance of the galaxies. When the velocities for these galaxies are plotted against their respective distances, the graph of this data is that shown in Fig. 7-7. Because of the internal motions of galaxies in a cluster, the velocities plotted in Fig. 7-7 are the mean value obtained from the measured radial velocities for a number of members of the cluster. In considering this plot we must remember that the velocity for a particular cluster may be obtained with an error of perhaps little more than 1% of its velocity; but the distances are not known with this precision, particularly for the more remote clusters.

7-8 The Interpretation of the Velocity-Distance Relation

In Fig. 7-7 it can be seen that the trend of velocity with distance may be represented rather well by a straight line through the origin of zero velocity and zero distance from our galaxy. The rate of change of velocity with distance is about 20 mi/sec per million light years. This means that, on the average, the radial velocity of a galaxy at 1 million light years would be 20 mi/sec; for one at 10 million light years the velocity would be 200 mi/sec; and at any distance, the recessional velocity would be 20 mi/sec multiplied by the distance in millions of light years.

The fact that all of these galaxies are receding from us does not mean

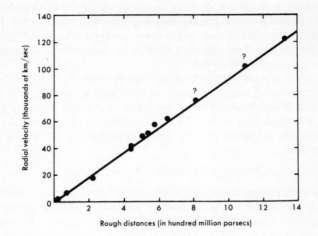

Fig. 7-7. **The velocity-distance relation for clusters of galaxies. (Reprinted from Abell's** *Exploration of the Universe* **by permission of the publisher Holt, Rinehart and Winston.)**

that we are at the center of the universe of observable galaxies. Imagine a large sheet of rubber which represents a two-dimensional universe and let there be scattered on this sheet a number of white dots to represent galaxies. Let our galaxy be one of them. Now slowly stretch the sheet at the same constant rate in both dimensions. From our own dot, all the other dots will be seen to be receding from ours. The more distant the dot the faster it will recede. This is exactly what is observed for galaxies. However, the same observations of radial motion from any other dot will show that all the others are receding from it, including our own. Transformed into three dimensions, this analogy will show that the universe will be observed to be expanding, no matter from what point it is observed.

If the relation is a linear (straight line) one between recessional velocity and distance, then the expansion must be in the nature of an explosion. At any time after the explosion of a hand grenade, the fragments most distant from the point of explosion (neglecting air friction and gravity) are those that have traveled the fastest. To find out how long ago the explosion of galaxies took place it is only necessary to compute how long it would require to travel 1 million light years at 20 mi/sec. The answer is about 10 billion years. Whether or not this is the age of the universe is a matter that will be discussed in the following sections.

7-9 *Cosmology*

In a broad sense *cosmology* refers to the structure, content, origin and evolution of the universe. There are a number of cosmological models of the universe and the only way we can choose between them is to decide which model agrees with the observations that have been made. There is no dearth of models, but there is a real scarcity of trustworthy, interpretable observations. Cosmology is a broad and intriguing subject. The following comments are to be considered only as a very brief introduction to the problem. It is hoped that the reader will consider the references given in the Appendix. One other matter which is almost a matter of embarrassment to the author is that in this short space it will not be possible to consider the impact of relativity theory on the whole problem. Something will be lost in the telling, but it will not be disastrous. Again, if you please, see the Appendix for further reading.

The observable universe of galaxies appears to be expanding; no other explanation suffices to explain the observations. If the velocity-distance relation is correct it implies that all the matter in the universe was in the same place about 10 billion years ago, and that at that time, for some unknown reason, it started to expand. Supposing that the explosion was of the hand grenade type, and that there was no gravitational retardation or further, no limiting velocity, the relation between velocity and distance will be a linear one over all distances. Under these assumptions the galaxies are all becoming fainter, and at some very distant time in the future even the brighter galaxies will be too faint to be seen. The universe will be infinite in extent. This theory of a common origin in time is often called the *Big-Bang theory*.

7-10   The Oscillating Universe

Is there any alternative to the situation outlined above? If there exists a gravitational attraction between the galaxies themselves (and why not?) one would expect the rate of expansion to decrease with time. If it is doing so, the straight line should change into a gentle curve sloping upward above the straight line and departing more and more from the straight line at greater and greater distances. The reason for this upward slope involves the travel time of light through space. The velocity of light is finite. The light we observe from a galaxy 5 billion light years distant left that galaxy 5 billion light years ago. Therefore, the Doppler shift that we measure for that galaxy now will be the value that it had when the light left it 5 billion years ago. If there is a slowing down of the expansion rate, we should observe radial velocities for the distant galaxies that give a higher expansion rate than for the nearby ones whose light left them only a short time ago. To find out what the universe is doing *now*, we should study the nearby galaxies; and to discover what it was doing *then,* we must observe the most distant galaxies. The observations in Fig. 7-7 reveal no upward trend above the straight line. However, some recent observations from the Mount Wilson and Palomar Observatories show a tentative upward trend above the straight line.

It is not necessarily true that a deceleration of the expansion rate will result in an eventual cessation of the expansion. It may be that the galaxies are already receding from each other at a velocity greater than the escape velocity, so that the universe will continue to expand for an infinite time. The escape velocity could be calculated if we knew the average mass density of the universe, but this would require a fairly accurate knowledge of the amount of matter in a given large and representative volume of space. Our present knowledge gives only a lower limit (see Sec. 7-7) and does not include the intergalactic dust and gas, and the dwarf galaxies that are so hard to observe.

If the universe is expanding at less than the escape velocity, at some distant time it should cease to expand and come to rest. Then the expansion of galaxies should reverse and a collapse begin. As some very remote time one would then expect all the galaxies to collide in some fantastic, explosive collision, after which, one presumes, the expansion would begin again. This would be an *oscillating universe*. The oscillations would continue for an infinite time in the future as they have done for an infinite time in the past. This possibility would avoid the necessity for a time zero, for a moment of creation.

The recent observations referred to at the end of the first paragraph of this section are now tentatively interpreted by Allan Sandage of the Mount Wilson and Palomar Observatories as suggesting an oscillating universe with a pulsation period of 80 billion years.

7-11   The Steady State Theory

Some remarks should be made about this unusual theory. In the preceding remarks it was assumed that the large scale appearance of the universe *now* is the same from any other point in the universe now. The steady state theory also assumes that the appearance has been the same for all *time*. Therefore, the universe as it appears now has been the same for an infinite time in the past and will be the same for an infinite time in the future. In this theory the space density of galaxies is always the same, in spite of expansion. Clearly this constancy requires that galaxies are *now* in the process of creation to replace those that are expanding out of sight, and to keep the mass density of the universe constant. The theory proposes that matter is actually being created now in the right amount per year to keep the mass density constant. This notion of continuous creation violates the law of the conservation of matter and energy. However, the amount that would need to be created each year is far too small to be detected by any known means. If the theory is correct there ought to be observable young, recently created galaxies that contain no old objects. At present, astronomers are uncertain how to judge the age of a galaxy. At first glance the steady state theory sounds improbable, but only because most scientists have developed such great faith in the law of conservation of matter and energy. The theory works and gives excellent results, but only within the limits of the accuracy of testing. The steady state theory must not be dismissed until it can be proven wrong.

7-12   Extragalactic Radio Sources

Most of the nearby galaxies are observed to be faint sources of radio noise which is emitted in much smaller amounts than the optical radiation. However, there is a relatively small number of galaxies whose radio radiation may be as much as a million times that of a normal galaxy. Since we observe radio radiation coming from all parts of the Milky Way, our own galaxy must be a radio source. In this respect it is a normal galaxy.

At the time of this writing, in mid-1965, a great deal of work is being done to explain why these peculiar galaxies have such a tremendous output of radio energy. Studies have shown that most of this energy is *synchrotron* radiation. Both theoretically and experimentally it can be shown that when a very high speed electron moves through a magnetic field, not only is its direction changed but it also radiates energy in all wavelengths with an intensity which increases with increasing wavelength. This behavior is contrary to the pattern of radiation from a hot body in the long wavelength region (see Sec. 3-12). This increase of intensity with wavelength is observed for the peculiar galaxies; because of this (and for other reasons) the radiation is assumed to be synchrotron radiation. The term "synchrotron" comes from the name of an electron accelerator which uses a changing magnetic field to accelerate electrons to very high velocities. The source of the magnetic field in these galaxies must be a source produced by currents of charged particles in motion. The high speed electrons are either produced in some explosive process or accelerated by the magnetic field itself, or both processes may operate. In our galaxy the Crab Nebula (Sec. 6-9), a strong source of synchrotron radiation, was produced by the explosion of a supernova. This hardly can be the real source of the synchrotron radiation from these unusual galaxies unless supernovae are occurring in these galaxies at an unbelievable rate.

Some of these peculiar radio galaxies look like ordinary galaxies, while others are misshapen in one way or another and look disturbed. At one time it was thought that the energy was released by the collision of two galaxies and that the energy was coming from the colliding interstellar clouds that were left behind between the two galaxies. Under such circumstances the radio energy should come largely from one area *between* the two separating galaxies. Instead, it is observed to come from two points on either side of an area that is bright optically. In a few cases, an explosion of some kind appears to have taken place in the nucleus of a galaxy, with the ejection of highly ionized gases in the two directions perpendicular to the galactic plane. This kind of explosion provides two clouds of gas that is emitting radio noise, one on each side of the galaxy. The reason for the explosion is unknown.

There is another class of extragalactic radio sources called "quasars" (for quasi-stellar objects) which are most unusual. These are exceptionally strong radio emitters, even stronger than the peculiar galaxies discussed in the last paragraph. In the ordinary visible region they are fairly bright, but in the radio region their brightness is so enormous that astrophysicists are hard put to think of a mechanism that could supply it. The gravitational collapse of a mass equal to many thousands of millions of suns and the release of huge amounts of nuclear energy is a possibility, but an uncertain one. When the problem is solved we shall have learned a great deal more about the behavior of matter under most unusual circumstances.

Only about three dozen quasars are known. On the whole their velocities of recession are large, and therefore their average distance is large. One of them, designated 3C9, is receding with a velocity of 149,000 miles per second, or 80% of the velocity of light—and the velocity of light, according to relativity theory, is the upper limit of all velocities. Another odd thing is that some quasars' optical radiation varies in intensity. A typical quasar emits as much energy as 100 galaxies. Its fluctuation in brightness is equivalent to the turning on and off of 100 billion suns in a year's time.

All of this points up the wonderful diversity among galaxies and the hope that astronomers may be on the threshold of an understanding of the universe of galaxies that was not even glimpsed five years ago.

7-13   The Origin and Evolution of Galaxies

In spite of many uncertainties it is possible to make some speculative remarks about the origin and evolution of galaxies. Let us start with the classification of galaxies into spirals, ellipticals and irregulars.

Color measurements show that the irregular galaxies are predominantly blue, the ellipticals red, and the spirals somewhere in between these two extremes. Referring to Sec. 6-14 on the evolution of stars, it has been calculated that after a star with a mass about that of the sun has spent a long time on the main sequence, it will evolve upward in brightness and to the right toward cooler temperatures on the H. R. diagram to a red giant stage. After this it will move rather rapidly to the left and down, crossing the main sequence above its original position and finally becoming a white dwarf. The same is pretty much true of other stars although there are variations in the pattern depending on mass. A star of much higher mass than the sun will reach the main sequence as a blue star, remain there for a time and then evolve to a red giant or supergiant stage. On the basis of this type of evolution, we would assume that the irregular galaxies are the youngest because of the predominance of blue stars, that the spirals are somewhat older, and that elliptical galaxies with their red stars are the oldest.

However, this suggestion runs into trouble with the Big-Bang theory, which proposes that at the moment when the expansion began all of the matter of the universe was in a relatively small volume. Shortly after the expansion began, the original mass of gas started to fragment into the large masses from which the galaxies were formed; i.e., all the galaxies formed at very nearly the same time and at the present time they are all of nearly the same age—about 10 billion years.

Another difficulty is that some recent work shows the masses of elliptical galaxies to be on the average considerably greater than the average spiral by perhaps as much as fifty times. How then could a spiral evolve into an elliptical galaxy? One possibility is the actual creation of matter within the spiral, or its accretion from intergalactic matter. Only the latter suggestion will be discussed. From what has been said in a previous section there is reason to believe that there ought to be considerable matter in intergalactic space which is not yet a part of the galaxies themselves. Perhaps when the spirals have a sufficient gravitational attraction to pull in the intergalactic matter, stars may, in time, be formed. We do know that the spirals have considerable amounts of interstellar matter from which to form stars and that the ellipticals do not. But if the ellipticals are so massive, why should not they acquire intergalactic matter and form stars themselves? The most massive of these would be blue; however, such has not been observed.

The situation is in a not very satisfactory state, but that is the usual condition in a rapidly developing field. In fact, it is this unresolved aspect of problems which has great appeal to scientists. A mass of observational data, plus a number of conflicting theories, present to the scientist a great challenge and one that he may well face with considerable enthusiasm. He also knows that in the solving of one problem he will uncover others that will challenge his attention and interest.

QUESTIONS

1. Summarize the several methods for the determination of the distances of galaxies. What would be the parallax in seconds of arc of the Andromeda galaxy?
2. Discuss the presence of interstellar material in the classes of galaxies and the consequences for the evolution of galaxies.
3. What is the evidence that galaxies are in rotation?
4. What might you expect to observe during and after the collision of two galaxies?
5. What difficulties are encountered in discovering new dwarf galaxies?

Appendix 1

Suggested Readings

The following text books are recommended:

The Exploration of the Universe, George Abell. New York: Holt, Rinehart & Winston Inc., 1964.

Principles of Astronomy, Stanley P. Wyatt. Boston: Allyn and Bacon, 1964.

Introduction to Astronomy, Dean B. McLaughlin. New York: Houghton Mifflin Co., 1961.

In addition to the above full-length texts, the articles which appear frequently in the monthly magazine *Scientific American* are recommended most highly.

The monthly publication *Sky and Telescope*, which is available in most libraries, is particularly directed to amateur astronomers. It is well written and highly informative.

A detailed and easily used set of star maps is contained in Norton's *Star Atlas and Telescopic Handbook* which, along with the magazine *Sky and Telescope*, may be obtained from the Sky Publishing Corporation, Cambridge, Massachusetts.

For those who might be interested in making a telescope, it is recommended that they obtain the book *Amateur Telescope Making* from the Scientific American, Inc., New York.

Appendix 2

Star Maps

The five star maps are charts of the brighter stars that can be seen in the sky by an observer in the Northern Hemisphere. On the four seasonal charts, right ascension is given along the top, and declination on the left side. The months along the bottom of each chart refer to the stars that will be (approximately) on the observer's local meridian at about 8 P.M. standard time. As the night progresses, the observer's local meridian moves from right to left across each chart. The declination of those stars that pass through the observer's zenith (overhead point) will be equal to the observer's latitude. On the circumpolar chart note that the pointer stars, a and β, of the Big Dipper (Ursa Major) point directly to the North Star (Polaris), which is a part of the Little Dipper (Ursa Minor).

Appendices 2A, 2B, 2C, and 2D have been reproduced, by permission, from *The Elements and Structure of the Physical Sciences* by J. A. Ripley, Jr., published by John Wiley & Sons, Inc. (1964).

APPENDIX 2A.   THE SPRING CONSTELLATIONS

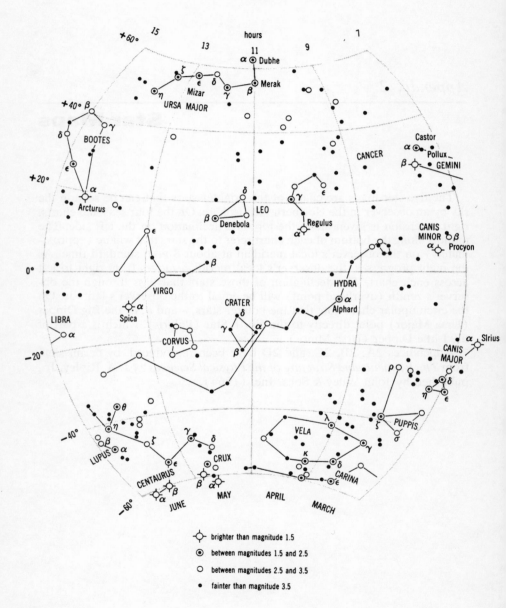

APPENDIX 2B.   THE SUMMER CONSTELLATIONS

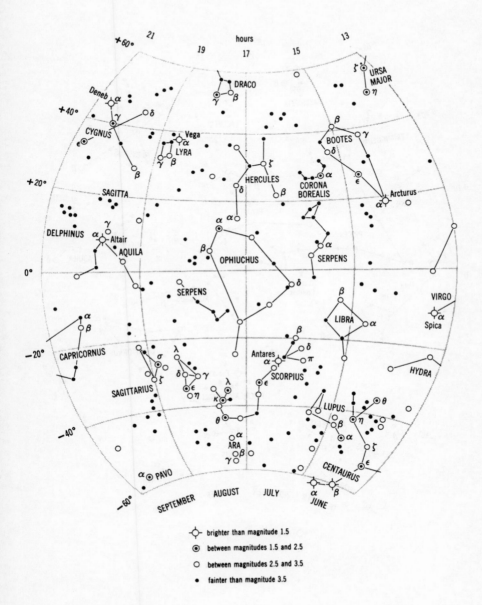

brighter than magnitude 1.5

between magnitudes 1.5 and 2.5

between magnitudes 2.5 and 3.5

fainter than magnitude 3.5

APPENDIX 2C.   THE AUTUMN CONSTELLATIONS

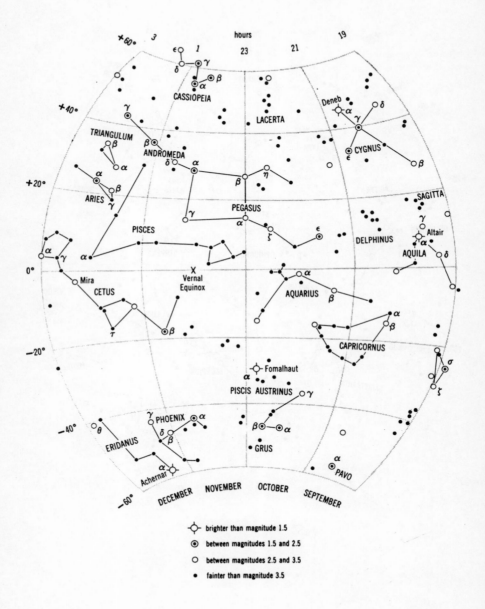

128

APPENDIX 2D. THE WINTER CONSTELLATIONS

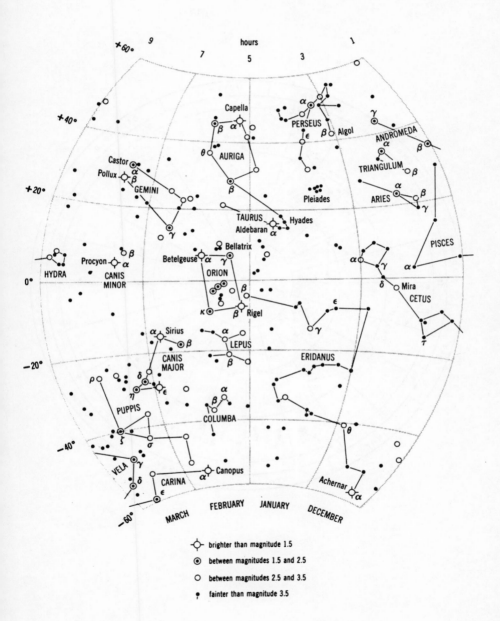

129

APPENDIX 2E. NORTH CIRCUMPOLAR CONSTELLATIONS

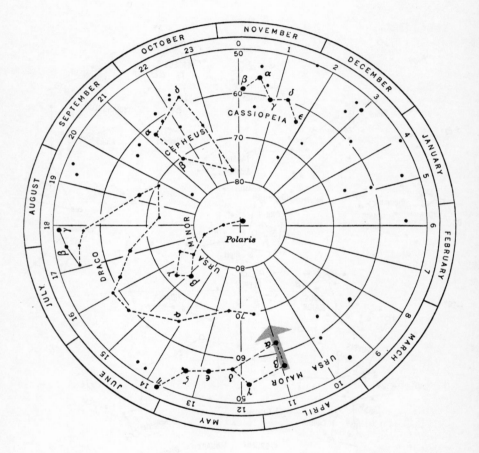

Index

Aberration, 15
Absolute magnitude:
  definition, 86
  spectroscopic, 83
Absolute temperature scale, 38
Almagest, 2
Andromeda galaxy, 109
Angstrom unit, 28
Angular diameter, 19
Aphelion, 9
Apogee, 19
Apparent magnitude, 85
Asteroids, 57
Astronomical unit:
  definition, 8
  measurement, 50
Atomic structure, 42

Binary stars:
  eclipsing, 95
  spectroscopic, 93
  visual, 92
Bode's law, 57
Bradley, 15

Celestial coordinates, 16
Celestial equator, 16
Celestial poles, 16
Celestial sphere, 16
Comets:
  appearance, 65
  masses, 65
  orbits, 67
  physical nature, 65
  relation to meteoroids, 67
Conjunction:
  inferior, 53
  superior, 52

Constellations, 83
Copernican system, 6
Copernicus, 6
Cosmology, 118
Crab nebula, 101

Declination, 17
Deferent, 4
Direct motion, 2
Dispersion, 29
Distance modulus, 86
Doppler effect, 46
Double stars, 92-96

Earth:
  density, 14
  diameter, 14
  mass, 14
  orbit, 16
  revolution, 15
  rotation, 14
Earthshine, 21
Eclipses:
  moon, 26
  sun, 26
Ecliptic, 16
Ellipse:
  eccentricity, 9
  focus, 9
  major axis, 9
  minor axis, 9
Elongation, 3
Epicycle, 3
Equinoxes, 16
Escape of atmospheres, 58
Evening star, 3

Foucault pendulum, 14

Galactic halo, 107
Galaxies:
  Andromeda, 109
  brightness, 115
  clusters, 115
  dimensions, 115
  distances, 114
  masses, 115
  origin and evolution, 122
  our own, 102
  radial velocities, 117
  radio sources, 120
  recession, 117
  redshift, 117
  types, 110-114
  velocity-distance relation, 117
Galaxy, our, 102
Galileo, 11
Geocentric system, 2
Gravitation, 12

Halo, galactic, 107
Harmonic law, 10
Heliocentric system, 6
Hertzsprung-Russell diagram, 89

Intergalactic matter, 116
Index of refraction, 29
Interstellar medium:
  dust, 103
  gas, 103
Interstellar reddening, 104
Ionization, 42

Jupiter:
  atmosphere, 59
  interior, 59
  orbital data, 52
  physical data, 52
  radio source, 60
  satellites, 62
  surface details, 59

Kelvin (absolute) temperature scale, 38
Kepler, 9
Kepler's laws, 9-11

Law of areas, 10
Lenses:
  aberrations, 30
  focus, 30
  properties, 30

Light:
  infrared, 28
  ultraviolet, 28
  visible, 28
  wavelength unit, 28
Light year, 8

Magellanic clouds, 111, 116
Maria, lunar, 23
Mars:
  atmosphere, 54-56
  existence of life, 56
  orbital data, 52
  physical data, 52
  Mariner IV observations, 56
  satellites, 54
  telescopic appearance, 54
  temperature, 56
Mass of a planet:
  determination, 63
Mercury:
  aspects from earth, 52
  general description, 53
  orbital data, 52
  physical data, 52
Meteor:
  definition, 66
  phenomenon, 66, 68
  showers, 66
Meteorites:
  age, 69
  composition, 67
  craters, 69
  definition, 66
  origin, 70
  Siberian (1908), 71
Meteoroid:
  atmospheric impact, 66
  composition, 67
  definition, 66
  relation to comets, 67
  structure, 67
  swarms, 66
Micrometeorites, 70
Milky Way, 102
Moon:
  atmosphere, 23, 59
  craters, 23-25
  mountains, 24
  orbit, 19
  origin of surface features, 23-26
  phases, 21

Moon:—*Cont.*
surface, 22-23
surface temperature, 22
Morning star, 3

Nebulae:
bright, 104
dark, 104
Neptune:
discovery, 63
orbital data, 52
satellites, 62
surface, 62
Newton, 12

Parsec, 8
Perigee, 19
Perihelion, 9
Period- luminosity relation, 99
Photon, 43
Planetary data, 52
Pluto:
discovery, 63
orbital data, 52
Precession, 18
Ptolemaic system, 2, 5
Ptolemy, 2
Pythagoras, 6

Quantum theory of light, 43

Radial velocity, 46, 84
Reflection, 29
Refraction, 29
Retrograde motion, 2, 6
Right ascension, 17
Roche's limit, 61

Saturn:
atmosphere, 60
interior, 61
orbital data, 52
physical data, 52
ring system, 61
satellites, 62
surface detail, 60
Seasons, 17
Solar system:
distance measurements, 50
origin and evolution, 71-75
scale, 50
two families, 51

Solar wind, 66
Solstices, 16
Spectral line, definition, 37
Spectral sequence:
description, 86
interpretation, 87
Spectral types, 86
Spectroscope, 37
Spectrum:
absorption, 40
continuous, 37
definition, 30
emission (bright line), 39
stellar, 86
theory and explanation, 43-46
Star clusters:
globular, 97
Milky Way, 96
Stars:
absolute magnitude, 85
apparent magnitude, 86
distance modulus, 86
distances, 84
eclipsing, 95
evolution, 105-107
formation, 105
giant sequence, 89
luminosity function, 91
magnitude system, 85
main sequence, 89
mass-luminosity relation, 91
nuclear reactions, 106
parallax, 84
proper motion, 85
radial velocity, 84
spectroscopic binaries, 93
visual double, 92
white dwarfs, 90
Steady state theory, 120
Stellar parallax, 8
Stellar populations:
Type I, 107
Type II, 107
Stellar spectra, 86
Sun:
chromosphere, 76
corona, 76, 80
coronal spectrum, 80
density, 76
effects on earth, 83
flares, 80
granules, 77

Date Due

Sun:—*Cont.*
  observing instru[ments]
  photosphere, 76
  physical structu[re]
  prominences, 76
  radio noise, 82
  reversing layer,
  spectrum, 82
  spots, 78
Sun spot cycle, 81

Telescopes:
  radio, 47
  reflector, 32
  refractor, 31
  resolution, 36
Tides, on earth, 20
Time, 19
Transit of a planet
Tycho, 7

Universe:
  expanding, 117–119
  origin, 122
  oscillating, 123
Venus:
  discovery, 62
  orbital data, 52
  satellites, 62
  surface, 62

Variable stars:
  Cepheid, 98, 108
  novae, 100
Vega:
  aspects from earth, 52
  apparent description, 99
  orbital data, 52
  physical data, 52

Zenith, 14
Zodiac, 16